M63-170

A FIRST COURSE IN EDUCATIONAL
STATISTICS

A FIRST COURSE IN
EDUCATIONAL STATISTICS

BY

EDNA E. KRAMER, Ph.D.

Assistant Professor of Mathematics
New Jersey State Teachers College
Montclair, New Jersey

LB
2846
K7
1935

NEW YORK
JOHN WILEY & SONS, Inc.
London: CHAPMAN & HALL, Limited
1935

COPYRIGHT, 1935
BY
EDNA E. KRAMER

All Rights Reserved
This book or any part thereof must not
be reproduced in any form without
the written permission of the publisher.

Printed in the U. S. A.

THE HADDON CRAFTSMEN, INC.
CAMDEN, N. J.

PREFACE

The material in the following text is the result of the author's experience with classes at the New Jersey State Teachers College at Montclair.

For the past few years, all sophomore students have been required to take a 52-hour course in educational statistics. Inasmuch as the students varied greatly with respect to mathematical background and ability, it was difficult to find a text to furnish so heterogeneous a group with the essentials of the subject in the limited time allotted to the course. The standard works in educational statistics proved too comprehensive, whereas "primers" and "drill-books" were inadequate.

Hence the author resorted, at first, to lectures and mimeographed notes, and finally embodied this material in a text lithoprinted by Edwards Brothers. This lithoprinted text has been used by several sets of students, and has been revised and enlarged to meet the difficulties encountered by them. The present text contains all these revisions and additions.

The material is presented with the hope that it may be of assistance to instructors and students in other colleges and normal schools who may be experiencing difficulties similar to ours. The author has attempted to attain the following objectives:

(1) To present in elementary fashion those statistical facts which form a necessary background for a proper understanding of educational literature and a minimum prerequisite for educational research.

Material has been selected with a view to avoiding details which might prove confusing in a first course in the subject. Emphasis has been placed on interpretation rather than computation, and numerical work has been stressed only where it is essential to a proper understanding of statistical formulas and processes.

(2) To reduce the mathematics involved to simplest form.

For the benefit of the student with little mathematical background, any arithmetic or algebraic facts needed, are developed at appropriate points. For example, there is work with square roots, interpolation, graphic methods.

On the other hand, the author has attempted to furnish logical, if elementary, justification of all facts and formulas. The Appendix gives a rigorous development of a number of formulas, for the benefit of students whose algebraic background is good.

(3) To stress the practical rather than the theoretic aspects of the subject.

The author has gone to some pains to select illustrative material from current educational periodicals rather than to resort to artificial or hypothetical data. She has attempted in this way to furnish students simultaneously with drill in numerical computation and practice in critical examination of real data.

The exercises in the text require students to find additional illustrative data in current periodicals, and, in this way, verify the application of the statistical processes developed in the text.

The author takes this occasion to thank Professor David R. Davis for reading the original manuscript and offering many valuable criticisms and suggestions. She wishes also to express her appreciation to President Harry A. Sprague and Professor John C. Stone, who sponsored and encouraged the use of experimental material with Montclair students. She is also indebted to the numerous authors who have graciously given their permission to use data from articles which they have written.

STATE TEACHERS COLLEGE
UPPER MONTCLAIR, N. J.
June 1, 1934

EDNA E. KRAMER

CONTENTS

A FIRST COURSE IN EDUCATIONAL STATISTICS

INTRODUCTION

THE TEACHER'S NEED FOR STATISTICAL KNOWLEDGE

Comprehension of Educational Literature. The modern teacher who is interested in new movements in the general field of teaching, or in new methods of instruction in some particular subject, will naturally have occasion to read the most recent educational texts, as well as articles in current issues of educational periodicals. For a proper comprehension of such literature, it is becoming increasingly necessary to possess at least an elementary knowledge of statistical terms and statistical methods. Such reading is very likely to include statements like the following:

The two mean scores are shown to be 5.6 before seeing the film. This is a shift in the direction of friendliness toward the Germans. The difference between these two mean scores is 0.38. $\sigma_1 = 1.43$ and $\sigma_2 = 1.11$. The probable error of the difference is 0.0708 so that the ratio of the difference to the probable error is 5.37. We seem to be justified therefore in concluding that the film "Four Sons" had a significant effect in making children more friendly toward the Germans.[1]

By considering the range for behavior-score medians from 47.5 to 88.3 one has a range that is 2.47 times the probable error of the distribution. The range of academic grade medians ranging from 71 to 89.3 and corresponding with a range of 40 to 115 in behavior scores is 2.54 times the probable error of the grade distribution.[2]

A teacher should be able to understand and interpret a table similar to Table 1. Words like *mean, median, mode, norm, range,* etc., should be part of the teacher's vocabulary. Terms like

[1] Ruth C. Peterson and L. L. Thurstone, "The Effect of a Motion Picture Film on Children's Attitudes toward Germans," *Journal of Educational Psychology*, April, 1932.

[2] Herbert Sorenson, "Some Factors for Pupil Control Measured and Related," *Journal of Educational Psychology*, January, 1932.

standard deviation and *correlation coefficient* should not be mere abstractions to him.

TABLE 1*

CORRELATION COEFFICIENTS

Composite scores	Correlation with algebra marks	No. of cases	Probable error
1. I.Q. and arithmetic................	0.66	112	0.038
2. I.Q. and Orleans test scores........	0.68	112	0.034
3. Or. Sc. and Ar....................	0.72	112	0.031
4. I.Q., Or. Sc., Ar..................	0.68	112	0.034

* Data from "Ability Grouping in the High School" by Ferdinand Kertes, *Mathematics Teacher*, January, 1932.

Educational Research. In making an experimental study or a school survey, a teacher should be capable of using statistical methods in reporting and interpreting his findings.

Graphic Methods. Even a teacher who may not need an extensive knowledge of statistical theory in connection with his reading may have occasion to give graphic representation to school data or to material which he wishes to present to his pupils in vivid fashion.

Testing and Rating Pupils. Every teacher will have frequent need to administer tests to pupils, whether these tests be of his own composition or standardized, and, what is more important, to interpret the results of these tests. For a proper handling of such results, the statistical method is essential.

Varied Needs. Other uses for the statistical method in the field of teaching might be here discussed, but instead, we shall proceed, in the first chapter, to a specific example.

CHAPTER I

ELEMENTARY STATISTICAL PROCEDURES

Treatment of a Set of Scores. The grades listed in the second column of Table 2 were obtained in a geometry test given to a group of 23 high-school students. After a week of drill, a second test was given on the same subject-matter. The grades obtained in the second test are listed in the third column of the table.

TABLE 2

Student	Test 1	Test 2
1	83	90
2	77	89
3	40	45
4	46	45
5	49	63
6	60	76
7	60	65
8	81	91
9	98	91
10	63	85
11	44	65
12	88	99
13	87	88
14	63	65
15	60	50
16	87	85
17	60	80
18	98	98
19	39	50
20	96	94
21	42	48
22	71	70
23	51	60

If you were the teacher of this group, what questions would you ask yourself in attempting to interpret the results of these

3

tests? You might ask some of the questions listed below. See if you can answer them.

Ex. 1. What is the "average" rating in Test 1? in Test 2?[1]

Ex. 2. What rating occurs most frequently in Test 1? in Test 2? Such a rating is called the *mode* (it represents the most fashionable rating).

Ex. 3. Is the mode of the first set of marks close to the average of the set? Answer the same question for the second set.

Ex. 4. Using the average ratings obtained in (1) as the basis of your judgment, compare the ratings of the group *as a whole* in the two tests. How would you account for the difference in results? Do the students who obtain high ratings in Test 1 obtain high ratings also in Test 2? Do the same students obtain low ratings in both these tests?

Ex. 5. Arrange the scores in each test in descending order of their magnitude. What is the rating of the student who stands at the head of the group in Test 1? at the foot of the group? at the middle point? (The rating of this student is called the *median*.) What is the *range* of ratings in Test 1? Compare the median rating with the average and the mode.

Ex. 6. Answer the same questions as in Ex. 5 for Test 2.

Ex. 7. The results of students 1, 2, 3, 4, 5 are represented in Fig. 1 by points *A*, *B*, *C*, *D*, *E* respectively. Copy this diagram and put in the points representing the other students. Note that the points are not scattered all over the graph, but seem to form a diagonal band.

Averages. The definitions of the terms used in the above questions are:

The *average* or *arithmetic mean* of a series of scores is the sum of these scores divided by the number of scores.

The *mode* of a series of scores is the score which occurs most frequently.

The *median* of a series of scores arranged in order of their numerical value is the middle score.

The *range* of a series of scores is the difference between the lowest and the highest scores.

In what follows, the term *mean*, or *arithmetic mean*, will be used instead of "average" since the latter is used to denote any

---

[1] Find these averages to the nearest tenth, i.e., carry to two decimal places and round off to one. For example:

63.43 becomes 63.4
63.47 becomes 63.5
63.45 becomes 63.5

one of the three *measures of central tendency—mean, mode,* or *median*—since each one of these indicates *the nature of a series of scores as a whole,* or *on the average.*

The *median* is a quickly determined measure, if the scores are arranged. The *mean* is most often used, since it is statistically most reliable. The *mode,* although not generally as important a measure as the other two, is occasionally more indicative as a

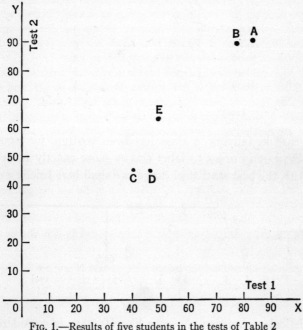

Fig. 1.—Results of five students in the tests of Table 2

measure of facts "on the whole." For example, in collecting for a school gift, in a class of 35 students, 30 students gave 25 cents each, 2 gave 10 cents, and 3 gave nothing. The mode, 25 cents, would be a better indication of the response of the students, as a group, than the mean, 22 cents.

The Frequency Distribution. In Table 3, the results of Test 1 (Table 2) have been grouped into a *frequency distribution,* by which is meant a *series of classes, and a set of corresponding frequencies.* The scores have been tallied in the fashion indicated.

The results of the test have been condensed by grouping the marks into classes. A *class-interval* of 10 was used in this classification, that is, the difference between the lowest score in each class and the lowest score in the next lower or next higher class is 10.

TABLE 3

Class		Frequency
90–99	/ / /	3
80–89	ᴫᴴᴛ	5
70–79	/ /	2
60–69	ᴫᴴᴛ /	6
50–59	/	1
40–49	ᴫᴴᴛ	5
30–39	/	1
Total		23

For ease in tallying, a class has been written, for example, as 80–89; but in order to label classes more exactly in accordance with the best statistical usage, we shall here briefly explain

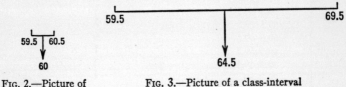

FIG. 2.—Picture of
a single score

FIG. 3.—Picture of a class-interval

a statistical convention. A score like 60, say, is considered to have as its geometric picture a segment or interval of unit length with 60 at the mid-point. See Fig. 2. The boundaries of this interval are thus 59.5 and 60.5. This is in accordance with mathematical usage, since a measurement of 60 is a measurement made "to the nearest unit," which means that it is not exactly 60, but nearer to 60 than to 59 or 61, that is, something between 59.5 and 60.5. Hence, the class designated as 60–69 above, has as its picture Fig. 3, since the lowest score in the class is 60, whose lower boundary is 59.5, and the highest score in this interval is 69, whose upper boundary is 69.5. Hence the boundaries of this class are 59.5 and 69.5, and a better designation would be 59.5–69.5.

Throughout this book we shall designate classes in this way, for this is the customary method when scores are *integral*, and our data will involve *integral* scores. If scores are not integral, there are other ways of writing the class intervals. For example, if measurements are very fine, the limits of class intervals may be written 50–59.99, 60–69.99, 70–79.99, etc., or 50–60–, 60–70–, 70–80–, signifying that all scores equal to the lower limit, and up to but not including the upper limit, are included in a given class.

Since the value of many statistical measures depends on the boundaries and mid-points of class-intervals, numerical results will naturally vary with the method of selection of boundaries.

Table 4 shows Table 3 written with classes listed by their boundaries.

TABLE 4

Class	Frequency
89.5–99.5......................	3
79.5–89.5......................	5
69.5–79.5......................	2
59.5–69.5......................	6
49.5–59.5......................	1
39.5–49.5......................	5
29.5–39.5......................	1
Total......................	23

Ex. 8. Make a table similar to Table 4 for the results of Test 2, using a class-interval of 10.

Histogram. Fig. 4 is a bar graph or *histogram* of the frequency distribution of Table 4. The base of each rectangle in this figure is the length of the class-interval, and the altitude is the frequency of the particular class.

Ex. 9. Make a histogram to illustrate the frequency table which you prepared in answer to Ex. 8.

Frequency Polygon. In Table 5 the results of Table 4 have been rewritten so as to indicate the mid-point of each class.

Since the size of the class-interval is 10, the mid-point of each interval was found by adding half of 10, or 5, to the lower

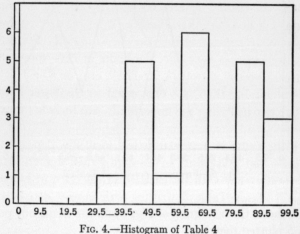

Fig. 4.—Histogram of Table 4

boundary of the interval. This is the way a frequency table is often written when it is to be used for approximate calculation or for graphic work. In such work, all scores in a class are regarded as concentrated at the mid-point of the class interval. A broken-line graph or *frequency polygon* of Table 5 is found in Fig. 5.

TABLE 5

Mid-point of class	Frequency
94.5	3
84.5	5
74.5	2
64.5	6
54.5	1
44.5	5
34.5	1
Total	23

Ex. 10. Rewrite, indicating the mid-point of each class-interval, the frequency table which you prepared in answer to Ex. 8, and then draw a frequency polygon to represent this table.

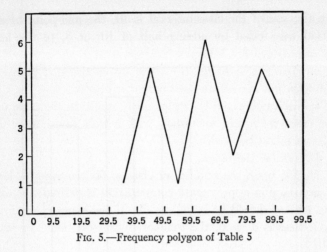

Fig. 5.—Frequency polygon of Table 5

Fig. 6 shows the histogram of Fig. 4 and the frequency polygon of Fig. 5 plotted together.

Rules for Grouping Data. Tables 3 and 4 indicate how a frequency distribution may be used to *organize a set of scores into compact form.* Of course, the use of such a table is hardly necessary for as small a set of scores as 23, but it is of great importance when the number of scores is large, since it would be

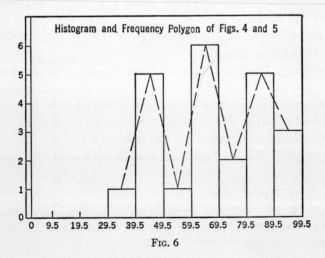

Fig. 6

difficult to study the nature of such scores in uncondensed form. The following rules are often observed in forming a frequency table from educational data:

1. Group data in 10 to 20 classes, rarely fewer or more. (In the illustration above, we used only 7 classes because the cases were few in number and the range fairly small. In the same way, if the cases were very numerous, with a wide range, more than 20 classes might be used.)

2. Determine the range.

3. Decide upon the number of classes. (If the range is large, or if accuracy in approximate computation is desired, the number of classes should be large, say 20. If the range is small and compactness is desired, the number of classes should be small, say 10.)

4. Divide the range by the number of classes to determine the class-interval. This will give the approximate size of the class-interval.

5. For computational purposes, class-intervals of 2, 5, 10, 15, 20 are the most convenient. Choose the number in this list nearest to the approximate value determined in item 4. If the approximate value is $2\frac{1}{2}$, choose 2. If the approximate value is $6\frac{1}{4}$, choose 5, etc.

6. Choose boundaries for your classes so that the lower boundary of the lowest class is slightly lower than the lowest score and the upper boundary of the highest class is slightly higher than the highest score.

Summary. In this chapter we have discussed various procedures connected with the study of a large group of scores. In order to *condense* such scores we have grouped them into a *frequency distribution*. We obtained a *graphic* representation of the group of scores by means of the *histogram* and the *frequency polygon*. We saw the need of computing an *average—mean, median,* or *mode*—in order to learn something of the nature of a set of scores *as a whole*.

EXERCISES

Ex. 11. The following scores in Army Alpha were made by a group of sophomores specializing in science at the New Jersey State Teachers College at Montclair: 198, 184, 182, 180, 173, 162, 153, 153, 127. Determine the arithmetic mean, median, mode, and range of this set of scores.

Ex. 12. The scores in Army Alpha of students specializing in French were 199, 177, 174, 169, 166, 164, 161, 156. Determine the median score of this set. *Answer:* In this case there is no middle score. The fourth and fifth scores are 169 and 166. The score, $167\frac{1}{2}$, midway between these scores, that is the $4\frac{1}{2}$th score, is called the median in this case. Compare the intelligence of this group as a whole with that of the group of science students in Ex. 11.

Ex. 13. The achievement scores of the students whose Army Alpha scores are given in Ex. 12 are 41, 38, 56, 44, 45, 42, 50, 40. Arrange these scores in numerical order, and find the median score. Find also the mean score and compare the two.

Ex. 14. The following are the achievement scores of a group of sophomores specializing in English. Tally these scores and form two different frequency tables, using class-intervals of two different sizes.

45	48	46	43	46	49
53	46	43	38	38	35
43	42	44	45	51	41
50	53	45	49	44	43
43	53	42	38	45	45
50	48	39	32	41	50
49	59	41	40	36	48

Ex. 15. On the same graph, make a histogram and a frequency polygon of the first frequency table of Ex. 14.

Ex. 16. On the same graph, make a histogram and a frequency polygon of the second frequency table of Ex. 14.

Ex. 17. Both the Army Alpha and achievement scores of the students of Ex. 11 are given below. Represent these data graphically, in the manner indicated in Fig. 1. Also compare their achievement, as a group, with that of the French students in Ex. 13.

Army Alpha	Achievement
198	37
184	36
182	43
180	34
173	44
162	32
153	39
153	40
127	46

Ex. 18. Make a histogram and a frequency polygon of the data in Table 6.

TABLE 6

SCORES IN THE THURSTON PSYCHOLOGICAL
EXAMINATION FOR HIGH-SCHOOL GRADUATES
OF 478 APPLICANTS FOR ADMISSION TO THE
NEW JERSEY STATE TEACHERS COLLEGE AT
MONTCLAIR

Class	Frequency
314.5–334.5	1
294.5–314.5	10
274.5–294.5	7
254.5–274.5	30
234.5–254.5	44
214.5–234.5	61
194.5–214.5	75
174.5–194.5	71
154.5–174.5	76
134.5–154.5	51
114.5–134.5	32
94.5–114.5	13
74.5– 94.5	5
54.5– 74.5	1
34.5– 54.5	1
Total	478

Ex. 19. The following are the scores in Army Alpha of 50 sophomores at the New Jersey State Teachers College at Montclair. Group these data into a frequency distribution, and make a histogram and frequency polygon of the result.

175	198	174	184	162
209	168	147	181	176
180	167	195	161	162
171	186	144	179	186
169	182	172	194	177
184	180	180	127	177
169	187	141	153	192
179	168	151	189	178
170	166	156	155	164
189	175	180	157	183

Ex. 20. Group the data in Table 7 into a frequency distribution, and make a histogram and frequency polygon of the result.

Ex. 21. Group the data in Table 62 into two different frequency distributions—one for the Army Alpha scores, and one for the achievement scores.

TABLE 7

INTELLIGENCE QUOTIENTS OF MONTCLAIR COLLEGE HIGH-SCHOOL STUDENTS (SEPTEMBER, 1932)

131	105	129	135	
128	122	137	122	103
119	142	130	123	112
132	118	137	129	112
132	116	130	131	111
114	117	116	109	143
138	127	128	133	127
136	121	120	92	111
112	117	121	99	123
125	125	112	127	119
129	116	128	129	127
146	131	128	119	116
102	108	125	110	131
139	133	107	142	142
106	104	114	138	112
121	126	112	128	118
123	121	135	127	109
93	129	114	126	113
135	118	94	117	114
107	116	101	125	118
100	115	143	112	132
118	114	114	100	145
117	152	119	105	119
99	152	101	135	118
127	107	117	141	99
120	133	119	153	135
126	153	133	153	137

Ex. 22. What is the purpose of finding an average of a set of scores?

Ex. 23. Which one of the three averages—mean, median, or mode—seems to you to represent best the nature of a set of scores as a whole? Why? Which average seems the least representative? Why?

Ex. 24. The mean of a group of 30 students in a certain test was 65. The mean of a second group of 50 students in the same test was 75. What was the mean score of the 80 students?

HINT: The mean score of the 80 students would be the sum of their scores divided by 80. Now 65, the mean of the first group, is found by dividing the sum of the scores of the first 30 students by 30.

$$30\,\overline{)\,\text{Sum}}$$
$$65$$

Hence this sum = $30 \times 65 = 1950$
Similarly, for the second group:

$$50\,\overline{)\,\text{Sum}}$$
$$75$$

Hence the sum of the scores of the next 50 students is $50 \times 75 = 3750$.
Hence the sum of the scores of all 80 students is 5700.

Ex. 25. The mean score of a group of 40 is 102 and of a group of 60 is 97. Find the mean of the entire group of 100.

Ex. 26. Find the mean score of the 200 students in Groups $A, B, C, D,$

Group	Number of students	Mean of group
A...............	50	30
B...............	75	32
C...............	40	45
D...............	35	28

Ex. 27. Find several illustrations of data grouped into a frequency distribution from articles in educational periodicals. The following are some of the periodicals which are likely to contain such material:

Educational Method.
The Elementary School Journal.
The American Journal of Psychology.
The Journal of Educational Research.
The Journal of Educational Psychology.
The Journal of Educational Sociology.
The Journal of Genetic Psychology.
The Junior-Senior High School Clearing House.
Psychological Clinic.
The Teachers College Record.
The Journal of Chemical Education.
The Mathematics Teacher.

CHAPTER II

APPROXIMATE CALCULATION OF AVERAGES IN A FREQUENCY DISTRIBUTION

Need for Shortened Methods. In Chapter I we discussed the *averages*, or *measures of central tendency—mean, median,* and *mode*—used to describe the *nature of a set of scores as a whole.* We saw how to determine these measures from a given set of scores. This process is a simple matter when the scores are few in number.

Suppose, however, that we wished to find the mean of 400 scores. Adding 400 scores is not a quick piece of arithmetic. To find the median it would be necessary to arrange 400 scores in numerical order, which, again, requires considerable time. The usual procedure is to group the data into a frequency table, and

TABLE 8*

DISTRIBUTION OF I.Q.'S OF 221 STUDENTS

I.Q.	Frequency
132.5–137.5	2
127.5–132.5	1
122.5–127.5	7
117.5–122.5	15
112.5–117.5	15
107.5–112.5	27
102.5–107.5	32
97.5–102.5	39
92.5– 97.5	36
87.5– 92.5	27
82.5– 87.5	14
77.5– 82.5	5
72.5– 77.5	1
Total	221

* Same source as Table 1.

15

then to determine the desired average by the approximate methods which we shall now study.

The Mode. First, let us see how to determine the *mode* from a frequency distribution. In Chapter I the mode was defined as the score of most frequent occurrence. For a frequency distribution, since the actual scores are not available, it is possible to obtain only a *crude mode*.

Assuming that all scores in a class are concentrated at the mid-point of the class interval, Table 8 becomes:

I.Q.	Frequency
135	2
130	1
125	7
120	15
115	15
110	27
105	32
100	39
95	36
90	27
85	14
80	5
75	1

According to the definition of the mode in Chapter I, 100 will be the mode of this distribution, since it is the score which occurs most frequently.

Thus, the *crude mode* may be defined as the *mid-point of the class-interval with the greatest frequency*.

The crude mode is evidently not the most precise average to use as an indicator of group results, since its value depends on the size of class-intervals and on the boundaries of these intervals.

For example, Table 9 shows two ways of regrouping the data of Table 8. The first method would give 97.5 as crude mode, and the second 102.5 as crude mode.

Thus the crude mode can often be made larger or smaller by increasing or decreasing the size of the class-interval, or by changing the positions of the boundaries of these intervals.

TABLE 9a

I.Q.	Frequency
132.5–142.5	2
122.5–132.5	8
112.5–122.5	30
102.5–112.5	59
92.5–102.5	75
82.5– 92.5	41
72.5– 82.5	6

TABLE 9b

I.Q.	Frequency
127.5–137.5	3
117.5–127.5	22
107.5–117.5	42
97.5–107.5	71
87.5– 97.5	63
77.5– 87.5	19
67.5– 77.5	1

Ex. 1. Find the crude mode in Tables 10 and 11.

TABLE 10*

ORLEANS ALGEBRA PROGNOSIS TEST

Scores (mid-point of interval)	Frequencies
189.5	1
179.5	0
169.5	2
159.5	1
149.5	3
139.5	8
129.5	16
119.5	22
109.5	29
99.5	23
89.5	22
79.5	27
69.5	23
59.5	16
49.5	12
39.5	9
29.5	5
19.5	2
Total	221

* Same source as Table 1.

TABLE 11

HISTORY SCORES OF 479 APPLICANTS FOR
ADMISSION TO NEW JERSEY STATE TEACHERS
COLLEGE AT MONTCLAIR

Class	Frequency
95.5–100.5	222
90.5– 95.5	97
85.5– 90.5	56
80.5– 85.5	37
75.5– 80.5	35
70.5– 75.5	11
65.5– 70.5	7
60.5– 65.5	5
55.5– 60.5	4
50.5– 55.5	4
45.5– 50.5	1
Total	479

The Median. Let us next treat the question of how to find
the median in a frequency distribution. In Chapter I, we defined the median of a series of scores as the middle score of the
series. To compute the median from a frequency distribution,
we redefine it as *that point in the distribution on either side of
which half the frequencies lie.*

Let us consider the data in Table 12.

TABLE 12

Class	Frequency
44.5–47.5	1
41.5–44.5	3
38.5–41.5	8
35.5–38.5	10
32.5–35.5	4
29.5–32.5	2
	$N^* = 28$

* N is used as the symbol for *number of cases,* or *total frequency.*

In order to find approximately the median of a distribution
we shall assume that the measures in any class-interval are distributed evenly throughout that interval. Fig. 7 is a picture of
the frequency distribution of Table 12.

There are 28 scores in all; hence the median is that point

above and below which there are 14 scores. Counting up from the bottom we find that the median comes in the interval 35.5–38.5. See Fig. 8 for an enlarged picture of this interval. It is evident that the median is at the point marked, and that the distance of this point from the lower boundary of the interval is $\frac{8}{10}$ the length of the interval.

$$\frac{8}{10} \times 3 = 2.4$$

Hence the median is $35.5 + 2.4 = 37.9$

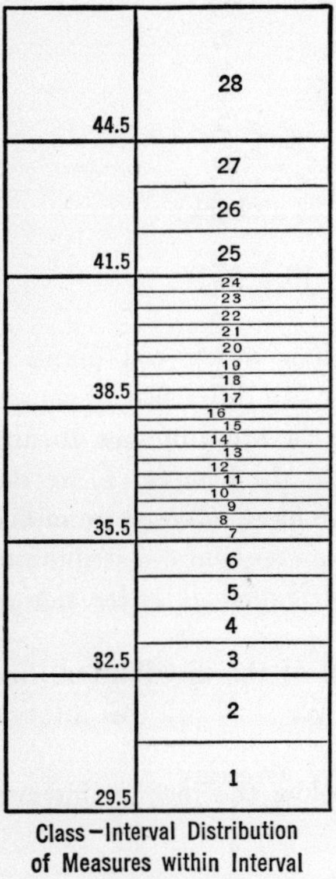

Fig. 7.—Frequency distribution of Table 12

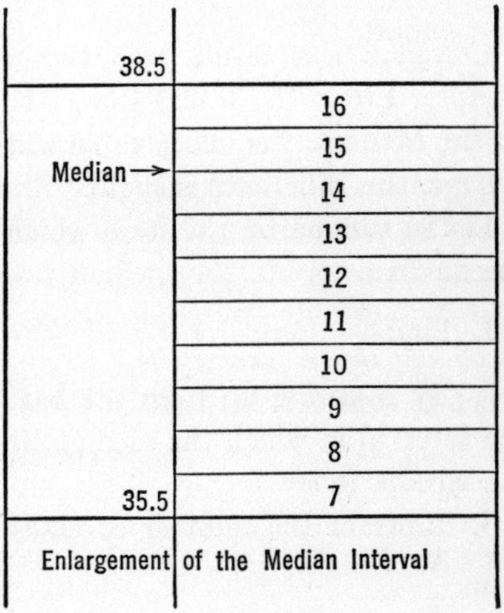

Class—Interval Distribution of Measures within Interval

Fig. 8

Enlargement of the Median Interval

Computing from the upper boundary the distance is

$$\frac{2}{10} \times 3 = 0.6$$

Median $= 38.5 - 0.6 = 37.9$, which checks the other result.

To compute the median in Table 4 in Chapter I, we seek the point above and below which $\frac{23}{2} = 11.5$ scores lie. Counting up from the bottom the median is in the class 59.5–69.5 with frequency 6. There are 7 scores below the class. Hence the median point is $11.5 - 7 = 4.5$ measures above 59.5. Since there are 6 measures in the interval 59.5–69.5, the distance of the median point from 59.5 is $\dfrac{4.5}{6}$ the length of the interval.

$$\frac{4.5}{6} \times 10 = 7.5$$

and the median $= 59.5 + 7.5 = 67.0$

Computing the median from above, as a check:

$$\text{Median} = 69.5 - \frac{1.5}{6} \times 10 = 67.0$$

Compare this result with the median which you found in Chapter I from the actual scores. There is a difference, of course. In the case of a frequency table where the total number of cases is *large*, this difference is slight.

Let us summarize the steps which we have followed in finding the median.

1. Find $\dfrac{N}{2}$.

2. By counting up from the bottom of the distribution, find the interval in which the median lies. We shall call this interval the *median interval*.

3. Subtract the number of cases below the median interval from $\dfrac{N}{2}$.

4. Divide the number in item 3 by the frequency of cases in the median interval.

5. Multiply the fraction in item 4 by the size of the interval.

6. Add the product in item 5 to the lower boundary of the median interval. The result will be the median. If we wish to put this in the form of a formula, let:

l = lower boundary of the median interval.

f = frequency of cases in that interval.

b = number of cases below median interval.

i = size of the interval.

Then:

$$M = l + \frac{\frac{N}{2} - b}{f} \times i$$

Ex. 2. By making up a set of rules for finding the median by counting *down* in the frequency distribution, show that

$$M = u - \frac{\frac{N}{2} - a}{f} \times i$$

where u = upper boundary of median interval.

a = number of cases above median interval.

Ex. 3. Find the median of the distribution in Table 8.

Ex. 4. Find the median of the distribution in Table 10.

Ex. 5. Find the median of the distribution in Table 11.

Ex. 6. Find the median of the distribution in Table 6 of Chapter I.

Percentiles. Although, in this chapter, we are dealing with averages, it would seem well at this point to define and discuss *percentiles* in a frequency distribution, since the process of computing them is so similar to the process of finding the median.

We define a *percentile as a point in a frequency distribution below which a given percentage of the frequencies lie.*

The 10th percentile in a frequency distribution is the point below which 10 per cent of the scores lie. The 15th percentile is the point below which 15 per cent of the scores lie, etc. The median is thus the 50th percentile. The 10th percentile is called the first *decile*. The 20th percentile is called the second decile. The 25th percentile is called the first *quartile*. The median is the second quartile. The 75th percentile is the third quartile.

Let us find the first quartile in Table 11.

Twenty-five per cent of 479 = 119.75. Counting up from the bottom, the first quartile is in the interval 85.5 − 90.5. There are 104 cases below this interval. 119.75 − 104 = 15.75. Since there are 56 cases in the interval containing the quartile, the distance of the first quartile above the lower boundary is

$$\frac{15.75}{56} \times 5 = 1.4, \text{ approximately}$$

Hence, the first quartile = 85.5 + 1.4 = 86.9.

Ex. 7. Find the 2nd decile and the 3rd quartile in Table 8.
Ex. 8. Find the 1st quartile and the 4th decile in Table 6.
Ex. 9. Find the 35th percentile in Table 10.

The Mean. Let us apply approximate methods of finding the mean in the frequency distribution of Table 5 of Chapter I. In this work, we shall consider all the scores in any class as concentrated at the mid-point of that class. The scores would then run

94.5
94.5
94.5
84.5
84.5
84.5
84.5
84.5 etc.

Instead of listing the 23 scores and adding, we shall shorten this work by employing multiplication.

$$94.5 \times 3 = 283.5$$

which is the sum of the first 3 scores.

$$84.5 \times 5 = 422.5$$

which is the sum of the next 5 scores.

Thus, we have

94.5 × 3	283.5
84.5 × 5	422.5
74.5 × 2	149.0
64.5 × 6	387.0
54.5 × 1	54.5
44.5 × 5	222.5
34.5 × 1	34.5
$N = 23$	1553.5

Dividing the sum by 23, we have

Mean = 67.5, approximately

If you compare this result with the result you obtained from averaging the true scores, you will see that they differ some-

what. The difference between the true mean and the mean found
by this approximate method, however, will be very slight when
the total frequency of cases is large. We must remember that
the example just treated involves only 23 cases.

Ex. 10. Apply the method just explained to finding the mean of the
distribution in Table 13.

TABLE 13*

SCORES IN SHORTHAND BY THE WORD METHOD

Scores (mid-point of interval)	Frequency
46	2
43	0
40	3
37	4
34	7
31	4
28	10
25	4
22	4
19	2
16	1
13	1
10	2

$$N = 44$$

*Taken from "A Comparison of the Results Obtained from the Teaching of Shorthand by the
Word-Unit Method and the Sentence-Unit Method," by Mildred Clark and O. A. Worcester, *Journal
of Educational Psychology*, February, 1932.

It is our object to shorten still further the work of approxi-
mating the mean. Suppose we were to find the mean of the scores
100, 86, 75, 65, 50. We might guess 75, the median, as a rough
approximation to the mean, and write:

$$100 = 75 + 25$$
$$86 = 75 + 11$$
$$75 = 75 + 0$$
$$65 = 75 - 10$$
$$50 = 75 - 25$$

$$\text{Sum} = 5(75) + 1$$

$$\text{Mean} = \frac{\text{Sum}}{5} = \frac{5(75) + 1}{5} = 75 + \frac{1}{5} = 75\frac{1}{5}$$

Ex. 11. Find the mean of 98, 90, 80, 72, 60, 54, 45. Use 72 as the estimated mean, and follow the method just explained.

Now we shall apply to Table 5 a combination of the two methods which we have just treated.

Since 64.5 is the mid-point of the median interval, its value is close to the value of the median, and hence to the value of the mean. We shall use it as our estimate of the mean.

We could write for the first 3 scores:

$$94.5 = 64.5 + 30$$
$$94.5 = 64.5 + 30$$
$$94.5 = 64.5 + 30$$

Instead of summing the right members we could multiply:

$$3(64.5 + 30) = 3(64.5) + 90$$

Similarly, the sum of the next 5 scores is

$$5(64.5 + 20) = 5(64.5) + 100$$

Thus we have:

Mid-point of class-interval	Frequency	
94.5 = 64.5 + 30	3	3(64.5) + 90
84.5 = 64.5 + 20	5	5(64.5) + 100
74.5 = 64.5 + 10	2	2(64.5) + 20
64.5 = 64.5 + 0	6	6(64.5) + 0
54.5 = 64.5 − 10	1	1(64.5) − 10
44.5 = 64.5 − 20	5	5(64.5) − 100
34.5 = 64.5 − 30	1	1(64.5) − 30
	$N = 23$	Sum = 23(64.5) + 70

Note that the coefficient of 64.5, the estimated mean, is equal to the total frequency of cases.

$$\text{Mean} = \frac{23(64.5) + 70}{23} = 64.5 + \frac{70}{23} = 64.5 + 3.0 = 67.5$$

the same result previously obtained.

Note that:

$$\text{Mean} = \text{estimated mean} + \text{correction}$$

and that the correction is obtained by adding the last column of figures and dividing this by the total frequency of cases.

Note also that the correction *may* be *negative*, since the sum of the last column of figures may be negative. A negative correction indicates too large an estimated mean.

This fact will save us much writing, since the last column of figures is the only one really needed. Let us see how this last column is obtained. The first figure, 90, is obtained by multiplying 30 by 3. The next figure is obtained by multiplying 20 by 5, etc. Hence all we need write is:

Mid-point of class-interval (X)	Frequency (F)	Deviation (ξ)	$F\xi$
94.5	3	30	90
84.5	5	20	100
74.5	2	10	20
64.5	6	0	0
54.5	1	−10	−10
44.5	5	−20	−100
34.5	1	−30	−30
	$N = 23$		Sum = 70

Estimated mean = 64.5
Correction   = 3.0
_____
Mean   = 67.5

Throughout this book, we shall use the following symbolism:

$$X = a \ score$$
$$x = X - M = \text{the } deviation \text{ of a score from the } mean$$
$$\xi = X - E = \text{the } deviation \text{ of a score from the } estimated \ mean$$

It is customary to use the Greek capital S, called *sigma*, and written Σ, to represent a sum. Hence the formula for the correction can be written:[1]

$$\text{Correction} = \frac{\Sigma F\xi}{N}$$

The numerical work could be simplified still further by measuring the deviations in class-intervals. Thus a deviation of 30 =

[1] An algebraic derivation of the formula for the correction will be found in Note I of the Appendix.

$3 \times 10 = 3$ class-intervals. (94.5 is obviously 3 class-intervals above 64.5.) $20 = 2 \times 10 = 2$ class-intervals, etc.

We rewrite the above work once more, giving ξ in class-intervals:

Mid-point of class-interval	F	ξ	$F\xi$
94.5	3	3	9
84.5	5	2	10
74.5	2	1	2
64.5	6	0	0
54.5	1	−1	− 1
44.5	5	−2	−10
34.5	1	−3	− 3

$N = 23$ $\Sigma F\xi = 7$ class-intervals $= 7 \times 10 = 70$

Correction $\dfrac{\Sigma F\xi}{N} = \dfrac{70}{23} = 3.0$

Estimated mean $= 64.5$

Mean $= 67.5$

(Note that the mean obtained is *approximate* since it is based on the assumption that all scores are concentrated at the mid-point of each class-interval.)

Let us work another example by this shortened method. A fairly good estimate of the mean in a frequency distribution is the mid-point of the median interval, or else the crude mode. It does not matter in any particular example what the estimated mean is, since the final result will be the same. The numerical work, of course, will be different for different estimated means.

We shall find the approximate mean of the distribution in Table 14.

TABLE 14*

A DISTRIBUTION OF THE INTELLIGENCE QUO-
TIENTS OF 404 HIGH-SCHOOL PHYSICS STU-
DENTS ACCORDING TO THE OTIS SELF-ADMIN-
ISTERING TESTS OF MENTAL ABILITY, HIGHER
EXAMINATION, FORM B

I.Q.	F
129.5–134.5	2
124.5–129.5	8

* From "A Study of Certain Mathematical Abilities in High School Physics," by William Ray Carter, in *The Mathematics Teacher*, November, 1932.

TABLE 14 (*Continued*)

119.5–124.5	35
114.5–119.5	43
109.5–114.5	61
104.5–109.5	65
99.5–104.5	54
94.5– 99.5	49
89.5– 94.5	44
84.5– 89.5	28
79.5– 84.5	12
74.5– 79.5	2
69.5– 74.5	1
	——
	404

TABLE 15

Mid-point of class-interval	F	ξ in class-intervals	$F\xi$ in class-intervals
132	2	5	10
127	8	4	32
122	35	3	105
117	43	2	86
112	61	1	61
107	65	0	0
			——
			294
102	54	−1	− 54
97	49	−2	− 98
92	44	−3	−132
87	28	−4	−112
82	12	−5	− 60
77	2	−6	− 12
72	1	−7	− 7
	——		——
	$N = 404$		−475

$$\Sigma F\xi = -181 \text{ class-intervals}$$

$$\Sigma F\xi = -181 \times 5 = -905$$

Estimated mean $= 107$

$+$ Correction $\dfrac{\Sigma F\xi}{N} = -\dfrac{905}{404} = \underline{-2.24}$

Mean $= 104.76$

It is evident, from this example, that the approximate method of finding the mean saves time, as the exact method would require the addition of 404 scores.

Ex. 12. Find by the short method the mean of the distribution in Table 13.

Ex. 13. Find by the short method the mean of the distribution in Table 8. Compare this with the mode found above for this distribution and with the median which you found in Ex. 3.

Ex. 14. Find the mean in Table 10 by the short method. Compare with the mode, and also with the median found in Ex. 4.

Ex. 15. Find the mean in Table 11.

Ex. 16. Find the mean in Table 6.

Ex. 17. Find mode, median, and mean in Table 16: (1) for the distribution of boys, (2) for the distribution of girls. Compare the achievement of the group of boys as a whole with the achievement of the group of girls.

TABLE 16*

DISTRIBUTION OF THE SCORES OF 404 HIGH-SCHOOL PHYSICS
STUDENTS ON THE KILZER-KIRBY INVENTORY TEST FOR
THE MATHEMATICS NEEDED IN HIGH-SCHOOL PHYSICS

Score	Boys	Girls
63.5–66.5	1	0
60.5–63.5	9	3
57.5–60.5	28	11
54.5–57.5	29	5
51.5–54.5	22	11
48.5–51.5	29	7
45.5–48.5	23	16
42.5–45.5	23	6
39.5–42.5	25	6
36.5–39.5	27	25
33.5–36.5	12	6
30.5–33.5	14	9
27.5–30.5	6	9
24.5–27.5	10	8
21.5–24.5	9	3
18.5–21.5	5	3
15.5–18.5	2	2
	$N = 274$	$N = 130$

* From "A Study of Certain Mathematical Abilities in High School Physics," by William Ray Carter, in *The Mathematics Teacher*, November, 1932.

CHOICE OF THE VARIOUS MEASURES OF CENTRAL TENDENCY

The Mode. The mode is used (1) when a rough measure of central tendency is sufficient, for, as we have seen, it can be very quickly determined in a frequency distribution; (2) as an *estimated mean*, as we have seen above.

The Median. The median is used (1) when ease of computation is desired. It is evident that, in a frequency distribution with a large number of classes and a high frequency, the finding of the median would involve considerably less computation than the finding of the mean; (2) when it is desirable to discount the effect of very high or very low scores.

In Table 14, for example, if the scores in the 3 lowest intervals were each 10 lower, the median would still be the same, whereas the mean would be altered.

If the scores in the highest intervals were all higher, the median would still be the same, whereas the mean would vary.

Thus the median is unaffected by these lowest and highest scores; the mean, on the other hand, is evidently influenced by all scores.

The Mean. The mean is used (1) when a measure of central tendency influenced by all scores is desired; (2) when it is needed for other statistical formulas and processes (for example, the coefficient of variation in Chapter III—later on we shall also see the use of the mean in the study of correlation); (3) when the greatest "reliability" (explained in Chapter VI) is desired.

Summary. In this chapter we have discussed the methods for calculating averages approximately in a frequency distribution. We have also listed the relative advantages of the various averages. The following exercises are meant to furnish applications of this material which are interpretative rather than computational in nature.

Ex. 18. A number of scores were grouped into a frequency distribution, and the mean, median, and mode were computed. After this was done, it was found that the five lowest scores in the group had each been raised 10 per cent. The frequency table was corrected, and the mean, median, and mode were computed again. Might any of this work be unnecessary; that is, could the mean or median or mode be unaffected by the change?

Ex. 19. If you wished to discount the effect of a few very low scores, which measure of central tendency would you compute in a frequency distribution?

Ex. 20. Which measure of central tendency is statistically most reliable? Which one is most quickly determined from a frequency distribution?

Ex. 21. A high-school teacher has two sophomore English classes, Group *A* and Group *B*. He notes that the mean English rating of each group the previous year was 75. Would he be justified in assuming that Groups *A* and *B* were similar material, and that he could employ similar techniques in teaching them?

Ex. 22. What aspect of a set of scores is not indicated by an average?

Ex. 23. Table 17 is taken from "A Study of Causes of Retardation among Mexican Children in a Small Public School System in Arizona," by O. K. Garetsen, *Journal of Educational Psychology*, January, 1928.

TABLE 17

MEDIAN MENTAL AGE IN MONTHS FOR AMERICAN AND MEXICAN PUPILS

Grade	Pintner-Cunningham Primary Mental Test (Verbal Test)		Meyers Pantomime Group Intelligence Test (Non-Verbal Test)	
	Americans	Mexicans	Americans	Mexicans
One	85.13	68.5	.....	.....
Two	98.00	89.0	88.0	84.0
	National Intelligence Test (Verbal Test)			
Three	106.0	81.0	102.0	86.0
Four	114.6	102.5	115.0	106.5
Five	132.2	127.0	123.5	140.1
Six	139.5	135.0	126.0	107.1
Seven	147.3	146.0	138.3	126.0
Eight	158.0	138.0	139.0	129.0

(*a*) Compare the median mental age of American children for each grade on the verbal and non-verbal tests. Do the same for the Mexican children. How can you explain the fact that the ages for the non-verbal tests are lower in general?

(*b*) Compare the median mental ages of the Mexican children in grades 3, 4, and 5 in the verbal and non-verbal tests. How can you explain these results?

(*c*) Find, for each grade, the difference in median mental age between American and Mexican children in both verbal and non-verbal tests. Compare differences for the verbal and non-verbal tests.

(*d*) What general conclusions might you reach from a study of these data?

(*e*) Why do you suppose that in this study the median was used as a measure of central tendency rather than the mean?

Ex. 24. Bring in material from articles in educational periodicals to illustrate the use of the various averages discussed in this chapter.

CHAPTER III

MEASURES OF VARIABILITY

Variability. In Chapters I and II we have seen how to indicate the nature of a group of scores by means of an average. Now there are some facts about the nature of a group of scores that an average will not reveal. If the average achievement of two groups of students is approximately the same, as indicated by a mean achievement of 75, let us say, it does not indicate that the nature of the two groups is the same. In the one group, the students may all have scores close to 75, that is, they may all be approximately average in achievement. In the other group there may be a number of students with very high achievement, some with very low achievement, and some with average achievement. In other words, an average does not indicate the *variability* of a group of scores.

One important educational question is the proper grouping of students into homogeneous groups, and hence it is natural that statistics should offer some way of telling whether a group is homogeneous or heterogeneous. By a *measure of variability* we mean an indicator of how a set of scores varies, on the whole, from some central score, as the mean, median, or mode.

The Range. In Chapter I, we have mentioned one measure of variability, the *range*, which is the difference between the lowest and highest scores in a set.

Let us show why this may not be a satisfactory indication of variability in all cases. In Table 18 the algebra grades of 24 students are listed in numerical order with the boys' grades in one column, and the girls' in the other. The range in the boys' marks is 80 and in the girls' marks 51, which would indicate that the boys form a more heterogeneous group than the girls.

31

TABLE 18

Boys	Girls
100	91
80	86
78	84
75	80
74	78
72	75
70	70
65	65
63	60
60	55
60	45
20	40

On further examination, however, we notice that the two extreme scores in the boys' marks, the highest and the lowest, really cause the large range. Excluding these, the range of the remaining 10 scores is only 20. If we were to exclude the end scores in the girls' marks, the range of the remaining scores would still be as large as 41. From these considerations, and from an examination of the marks themselves, it is certainly evident that the girls' marks are really more variable than the boys'.

Thus we see that the range is not a satisfactory measure because it is influenced too much by extreme scores. In order to get a better measure, the statistical procedure is to cut off not only the two extreme scores, but a number of scores from each end.

The Semi-interquartile Range. As a matter of fact, it is customary to cut off the top 25 per cent of the cases, and the bottom 25 per cent as well, and to consider the range of the middle 50 per cent of the cases in a frequency distribution. Then Q_3 and Q_1 are found, and $Q_3 - Q_1$ is called the *interquartile range*. It is customary to find half of this, and to use as a measure of variability the *semi-interquartile range*:

$$Q = \frac{Q_3 - Q_1}{2}$$

Thus, in Table 8:

$$Q_3 = 112.5 - \frac{15.25}{27} \times 5 = 109.68$$

$$Q_1 = 92.5 + \frac{8.25}{36} \times 5 = 93.64$$

and the semi-interquartile range

$$Q = \frac{109.68 - 93.64}{2} = 8.02 = 8.0 \text{ (to the nearest tenth)}$$

Ex. 1. Find the semi-interquartile range in Tables 11, 13, 6, 14, and 16. In 16 compare the variability of the group of boys with that of the group of girls.

Before proceeding to a discussion of other measures of the variability of a group, let us say that the *semi-interquartile range is the measure of variability most quickly and most easily determined when data are grouped into a frequency distribution.*

The Mean Deviation. Table 19 shows the results of 2 students working on a laboratory problem in physics, the purpose of which was to determine the weight of an object. The first student obtains 9.02 grams and the second student obtains 8.93 grams as the mean weight. The true weight of the object (to the nearest hundredth) is 8.96 grams. Does the second student deserve a better rating for his laboratory experiment, since his final result is closer to the true weight? If we assume that the instruments used by both students were correctly adjusted and equally fine, then the individual results of the first student show him to be more accurate in his work than the second. All the results of the first student are fairly close to the true weight and to the mean which he obtained. Most of the second student's results differ widely both from the true weight and the mean weight which he obtained.

TABLE 19
WEIGHT OF OBJECT IN GRAMS

Results of first student	Results of second student
8.91	8.71
9.10	9.10
9.15	8.90
9.08	9.02
8.94	8.65
9.09	9.21
8.89	8.55
8.96	9.33
Mean 9.02	Mean 8.93

The deviations from the mean for the first student (neglecting signs, since we are now interested merely in the magnitude of a deviation) are:

$$
\begin{aligned}
&0.11 \\
&0.08 \\
&0.13 \\
&0.06 \\
&0.08 \\
&0.07 \\
&0.03 \\
&0.06 \\
\hline
&0.62
\end{aligned}
$$

Mean deviation $= \dfrac{0.62}{8} = 0.08$, approximately

Those for the second student are:

$$
\begin{aligned}
&0.22 \\
&0.17 \\
&0.03 \\
&0.09 \\
&0.28 \\
&0.28 \\
&0.38 \\
&0.40 \\
\hline
&1.85
\end{aligned}
$$

Mean deviation $= \dfrac{1.85}{8} = 0.23$, approximately

Thus we see that the deviations for the first student on individual experiments vary from 0.03 to 0.11, and the average size of a deviation is 0.08; for the second student the deviations vary from 0.03 to 0.40 and the average size is 0.23.

Comparing the average or mean deviations for the students, it is seen that the mean deviation of the second student is almost three times as great as for the first, which indicates the greater variability of his results.

This example serves to illustrate, then, a second measure of variability, namely, the *mean deviation from the mean*, which is the mean of the deviations from the mean of a set of scores. The deviation of a single score shows how much it varies from the mean of the set, and hence the *average*, or *mean of these deviations*, will show how the set *varies as a whole*.

Let us find the *mean deviation from the mean* of the set of boys' marks in Table 18. The mean of this set of scores (to the nearest unit) is 68. We list the scores, and, beside each one, the deviation from 68 (omitting signs once more, as above):

Mark	Magnitude of deviations from the mean
100	32
80	12
78	10
75	7
74	6
72	4
70	2
65	3
63	5
60	8
60	8
20	48
Mean 68 (to the nearest unit)	145

$$\text{Mean deviation} = \frac{145}{12} = 12, \text{ approximately}$$

We see that the formula for the mean deviation is:

$$\text{Mean deviation} = \frac{\Sigma|x|}{N}$$

where $|x|$ is the mathematical symbol for the *absolute value* or *magnitude* of x. By the absolute value of x is meant the numerical value of x without regard to sign.

Sometimes deviations are taken from the median, instead of from the mean, in which case we specify that we are finding the *mean deviation from the median*. The median of the set of marks just handled is 71, and the magnitudes of the deviations from the median are given here:

Deviations from Median
29
9
7
4
3
1
1
6
8
11
11
51
141

$$\text{Mean deviation from the median} = \frac{141}{12} = 12, \text{ approximately}$$

Ex. 2. Find the mean deviation from the mean and the mean deviation from the median for each of the two sets of scores in Table 20. (Find means, medians, and deviations to the nearest unit only.)

TABLE 20*

SCORES OF 25 ELEMENTARY SCHOOL PUPILS IN THE OTIS CLASSIFICATION TEST, PART II, FORM B, AND THE SANGREN-WOODY READING TEST, FORM A

Pupil	Intelligence score	Reading score
1	60	136
2	57	85
3	56	103
4	55	103
5	52	89
6	42	92
7	42	91
8	42	120
9	42	74
10	36	55
11	39	59
12	38	55
13	36	81
14	35	64
15	35	78
16	26	76
17	25	61
18	24	72
19	22	83
20	21	74
21	19	53
22	17	38
23	15	35
24	14	45
25	12	29

* H. S. Hill, "A Common Denominator for Test Scores," *Elementary School Journal*, June, 1930.

Ex. 3. Find the mean deviation from the mean and the mean deviation from the median for the two sets of scores in Table 2. (Find means, medians, and deviations to the nearest unit only.)

Use of a Table of Squares and Square Roots. Before treating the most important measure of variability, we shall enter upon some preliminary arithmetic considerations involved in the use of a table of squares and square roots. Such a table appears on

p. 203 of this book, and the student will find it a great aid to him in computing the measure of variability which we shall next discuss, as well as in all subsequent computation.

Ex. 4. Using the table, find squares of the following numbers: (a) 47. (b) 376. (c) 37.6. (d) 3.76. (e) 0.54. (f) 1.86. (g) 0.186. (h) 4560. (i) 45,600. (j) 8700. (k) 9.46.

Ex. 5. Find square roots of the following: (a) 79. (b) 631. (c) 946. (d) 8.76. (e) 35,600.

In using the table of square roots, the student will find the following principle helpful:

If a number is multiplied or divided by any power of 100, the significant figures in its square root will remain unchanged.

As an illustration of this fact, we offer the following example. From the table:

$$\sqrt{186} = 13.6382.$$
$$\sqrt{18,600} = \sqrt{186 \times 100} = 10\sqrt{186} = 10(13.6382) = 136.382.$$
$$\sqrt{1.86} = \sqrt{\frac{186}{100}} = \frac{1}{10}\sqrt{186} = 1.36382.$$
$$\sqrt{1,860,000} = \sqrt{186 \times 10,000} = 100\sqrt{186} = 1363.82.$$
$$\sqrt{0.0186} = \sqrt{\frac{186}{10,000}} = \frac{1}{100}\sqrt{186} = 0.136382.$$

The principle may also be stated as follows: *Moving the decimal point an even number of places to right or left will not change the significant figures in the square root of a number.*

We shall show how to make use of this principle in several examples.

$\sqrt{0.0375}$ cannot be found directly from the table.

Moving the decimal point 4 places to the right, we have, from the table:

$$\sqrt{375} = 19.3649$$
Then $$\sqrt{0.0375} = 0.193649.$$

To find $\sqrt{97,600}$, we use the table to find

$$\sqrt{976} = 31.2410$$
$$\therefore \sqrt{97,600} = 312.410$$

Ex. 6. Using the table, find the square roots of:

(a) 0.0739. (b) 0.000632. (c) 8.74. (d) 9700. (e) 35,600. (f) 0.087. (g) 6.7. (h) 0.007. (i) 0.0087.

Since the square root table in this book does not give directly
the square roots of numbers with more than three significant
figures, we shall explain how square roots of numbers with more
than three significant figures can be found approximately by a
process called *interpolation*.

For $\sqrt{187.4}$, we have

$$
1\left[\begin{array}{l} 188 \\ 0.4\left[\begin{array}{l} 187.4 \\ 187 \end{array}\right. \end{array}\right.
\begin{array}{l} \text{Square root} \\ 13.7113 \\ \left.\begin{array}{l} \\ 13.6748 \end{array}\right]? \end{array} \right]0.0365
$$

In increasing from 187 to 187.4, the number has changed by
0.4. In increasing from 187 to 188, the number has changed by 1.

Hence, assuming that changes in the square root are proportional to changes in the number (a fact which is only *approximately* true), we have:

$$\frac{0.4}{1} = 0.4 \text{ of the total change in square root}$$

$$0.4 \times 0.0365 = 0.0146$$

and the required square root is

$$13.6748 + 0.0146 = 13.6894$$

To find $\sqrt{87.25}$ we have:

Number   Square root

$$
1\left[\begin{array}{l} 88 \\ 0.25\left[\begin{array}{l} 87.25 \\ 87 \end{array}\right. \end{array}\right.
\begin{array}{l} 9.3808 \\ \left.\begin{array}{l} \\ 9.3274 \end{array}\right]? \end{array} \right]0.0534
$$

$$0.25 \times 0.0534 = 0.0134$$
$$\sqrt{87.25} = 9.3274 + 0.0134 = 9.3408$$

To find $\sqrt{4596}$, we note that the significant figures in the
answer will be the same as for $\sqrt{45.96}$:

Number   Square root

$$
1\left[\begin{array}{l} 46 \\ 0.96\left[\begin{array}{l} 45.96 \\ 45 \end{array}\right. \end{array}\right.
\begin{array}{l} 6.7823 \\ \left.\begin{array}{l} \\ 6.7082 \end{array}\right]? \end{array} \right]0.0741
$$

$$\sqrt{45.96} = 6.7082 + 0.96(0.0741) = 6.7082 + 0.0711 = 6.7793$$
$$\sqrt{4596} = 67.793$$

Ex. 7. Using the square root table and interpolation, find the square root of: (*a*) 693.6. (*b*) 37.18. (*c*) 6125. (*d*) 0.6125. (*e*) 0.3746. (*f*) 3890. (*g*) 1.1036. (*h*) 7.834. (*i*) 0.718.

The Standard Deviation. We come now to the measure of variability which is most important from the statistical point of view, since it is the most reliable measure, and has most application in statistical theory. This measure is called the *standard deviation*, and is symbolized by the small Greek sigma, σ. The formula for the standard deviation of a set of scores is:

$$\sigma = \sqrt{\frac{\Sigma x^2}{N}}$$

where *x* represents deviation from the mean.

Let us treat the set of boys' scores in Table 18. Again, deviations from the mean are found; and again, since we are interested in the magnitude of these deviations, and not in the sign, we avoid the question of signs, this time by squaring the deviations, thus making all results positive.

Mark	x	x^2
100	31.9	1017.61
80	11.9	141.61
78	9.9	98.01
75	6.9	47.61
74	5.9	34.81
72	3.9	15.21
70	1.9	3.61
65	− 3.1	9.61
63	− 5.1	26.01
60	− 8.1	65.61
60	− 8.1	65.61
20	−48.1	2313.61

Mean = 68.1 Σx^2 = 3838.92

$$\frac{\Sigma x^2}{N} = \frac{3838.92}{12} = 319.91$$

$\sigma = \sqrt{319.91} = 17.6 = 18$, to the nearest unit

After squaring the deviations, the results are added, and, as before, the sum is divided by the total frequency, and then the square root of the result is taken, in order to undo, somewhat, the result of squaring the deviations originally.

Note that we have obtained σ correct to the nearest unit. This necessitates working out the mean and the deviations to tenths.

Ex. 8. Find the standard deviation of the set of girls' marks in Table 18, computing the answer to the nearest unit. Use the table for finding squares and square roots.

Ex. 9. The I.Q.'s of a group of students are 125, 120, 116, 110, 100, 100, 98, 95, 92, 85. Find σ to the nearest unit. Use the table for finding squares and square roots.

Ex. 10. Find σ to the nearest unit for the scores 92, 86, 82, 79, 76, 75, 75, 65, 60, 40, 15.

In the examples which you have just worked, you computed the standard deviation for a small set of scores. You can see that the numerical work involved would be enormous if the number of scores were large and if accuracy to several decimal places were desired. Just as in the case of finding an average, to find σ when the number of scores is large, these scores are grouped into a distribution and shortened methods are employed.

To illustrate the problem, suppose we were to find σ (to the nearest unit) in the following table:

Score	F
90	2
85	3
80	4
75	6
70	3
65	2
60	1
	$N = 21$

Evidently this table could be written

Score
90
90

85
85
85
80
80
80
80 etc.

and σ could be found as usual.

$$\text{Mean} = \frac{90 \cdot 2 + 85 \cdot 3 + 80 \cdot 4 + \ldots + 60 \cdot 1}{21} = 76.4$$

Instead of writing

Score	x	x^2
90	13.6	184.96
90	13.6	184.96
85	8.6	73.96
85	8.6	73.96
85	8.6	73.96
etc.		

we can write

$$184.96 \times 2 = 369.92$$
$$73.96 \times 3 = 221.88$$
$$12.96 \times 4 = 51.84$$
etc.

that is, we can use multiplication instead of addition to shorten the work somewhat.

Hence, the work for computing σ becomes:

x	x^2	F	Fx^2
13.6	184.96	2	369.92
8.6	73.96	3	221.88
3.6	12.96	4	51.84
− 1.4	1.96	6	11.76
− 6.4	40.96	3	122.88
−11.4	129.96	1	129.96
−16.4	268.96	1	268.96

Sum = 1177.20

$$\sigma = \sqrt{\frac{1177.20}{21}} = \sqrt{56.05} = 7.4 = 7, \text{ to the nearest unit}$$

When scores are grouped in this way, we evidently sum the

Fx^2 column instead of the x^2 column, as we did for ungrouped scores. It is evident then that the formula for σ, when *scores are grouped*, is

$$\sigma = \sqrt{\frac{\Sigma F x^2}{N}}$$

Now, even if scores are grouped, the above computation can become excessive if N is large, and hence it is desirable to shorten the work still further.

Once again, an estimated mean is used, and the deviations from this mean are computed. *If scores are grouped and deviations are taken from an estimated mean*, the above formula for σ is transformed into the form[1]

$$\sigma = \left[\sqrt{\frac{\Sigma F \xi^2}{N} - c^2} \right] \times i$$

where ξ represents deviation from the *estimated* mean.

c represents the correction to this mean.

ξ and c are measured in class-intervals.

i is the size of the class-interval.

Let us find σ for the frequency distribution of Table 21.

TABLE 21*

Class (Scores in shorthand by sentence method)	Frequency
47.5–50.5	4
44.5–47.5	1
41.5–44.5	7
38.5–41.5	3
35.5–38.5	10
32.5–35.5	7
29.5–32.5	3
26.5–29.5	1
23.5–26.5	3
20.5–23.5	1
17.5–20.5	0
14.5–17.5	3
11.5–14.5	0
8.5–11.5	1

$$N = 44$$

* Same source as Table 13.

[1] An algebraic derivation of this formula will be found in Note II of the Appendix.

Mid-point of class	F	ξ (in class-intervals)	$F\xi$		$F\xi^2$
49............	4	4	16 ⎤		64
46............	1	3	3 ⎥ 36		9
43............	7	2	14 ⎥		28
40............	3	1	3 ⎦		3
37............	10	0	0		0
34............	7	−1	− 7 ⎤		7
31............	3	−2	− 6 ⎥		12
28............	1	−3	− 3 ⎥		9
25............	3	−4	−12 ⎥		48
22............	1	−5	− 5 ⎬ −63		25
19............	0	−6	0 ⎥		0
16............	3	−7	−21 ⎥		147
13............	0	−8	0 ⎥		0
10............	1	−9	− 9 ⎦		81
			—		—
	$N = 44$		−27 Class-intervals		433

Estimated mean = 37

$c = \dfrac{\Sigma F\xi}{N} = -\dfrac{27}{44} = -0.61$ class-interval $\qquad \dfrac{\Sigma F\xi^2}{N} = \dfrac{433}{44} = 9.8409$

$\sigma = \sqrt{\dfrac{\Sigma F\xi^2}{N} - c^2}$ class-intervals $= \sqrt{9.8409 - 0.3721}$ class-intervals

$\qquad = \sqrt{9.4688} = 3.07$ class-intervals

$\qquad = 3.07 \times 3 = 9.21 = 9.2$ (to the nearest tenth).

Note that the columns ξ, $F\xi$ are found just as in finding the mean. The column $F\xi^2$ is found by multiplying results in the ξ and $F\xi$ columns.

Note also that, in order to give an answer correct to tenths, we have carried work out to the hundredths place until the very end, where we have rounded off to tenths. In order to obtain a square root to *two* places, it was necessary to keep *four* places under the radical sign.

Ex. 11. Find σ in Table 13. **Ex. 13.** Find σ in Table 10.

Ex. 12. Find σ in Table 8. **Ex. 14.** Find σ in Tables 6, 11, 14, and 16.

The Coefficient of Variation. Suppose that we are comparing two groups in which we have:

	Mean	σ
1st group............	60	7
2nd group..........	80	7

We might first judge that the groups were equally variable, but we must remember that the σ's are found by working with deviations from the mean.

Now, let us think, say, of a deviation of 5 from the mean of the first group, and an equal deviation from the mean of the second group. For the first group, this deviation is $\frac{1}{12}$ of the mean. For the second group it is $\frac{1}{16}$ of the mean. Hence this deviation is more significant in the case of the first group. In other words, the significance of a deviation, and hence of a σ, depends not only on its magnitude, but also on the size of the mean. Pearson has given a *coefficient of variation*:

$$V = \frac{100\sigma}{M}$$

(where M represents the mean) which takes account of this fact.

Finding the coefficient of variation of the first group above, we have:

$$V = \frac{700}{60} = 11.7$$

and for the second group:

$$V = \frac{700}{80} = 8.8$$

Hence, we see that the first group is more variable than the second.

Ex. 15. Find the coefficients of variation in Tables 13 and 8. Use the values of M and σ which you have found in previous examples.

Combination of Test Scores. When a number of different tests have been given to a pupil, the question arises how to combine the results in the different tests into one composite score.

A procedure often followed is to find the mean of the results. But these results may be expressed in different units—one test may be scored on a basis of 100, another on the basis of 5, still another may be a standardized test in which results are expressed in terms of age norms. Thus, a student's ratings might be 85, 19, 13 years 6 months, etc.

Now there are a number of ways in which test scores can be combined. At this point we shall treat just one such method, namely, one which makes use of the measure of variability σ with which we have just been working.

We define the *standard score* as: Standard score $= \dfrac{x}{\sigma}$, where x is the deviation of a score from the mean score, and σ is the standard deviation of the scores.

Below are the results of four different tests:

Mean	σ	Scores of a particular student in these tests	x	$\dfrac{x}{\sigma}$ (Standard score)
(1) 75	7	80	5	0.71
(2) 110	10	105	−5	− .50
(3) 7.2	0.8	7.5	0.3	.38
(4) 16.5	2.1	18.3	1.8	.86
				Sum = 1.45

The student's composite score would then be the mean of the standard scores in the last column:

$$\text{Mean} = \frac{1.45}{4} = 0.36$$

Ex. 16. Find the standard scores of the student in each of the following tests, and find his composite score in all of them:

Mean	σ	Score of the student
(1) 32	4	33
(2) 12.5	2.1	13
(3) 115	10.3	119
(4) 7.7	1.1	6.5
(5) 70	8.2	75

CHOICE OF THE MEASURES OF VARIABILITY

The Range. The range is used only for a quick, crude estimate of variability.

The Semi-Interquartile Range. Q is used: (1) when ease of computation is desired; (2) when the effect of extreme scores is to be discounted.

The Mean Deviation. The mean deviation is not used as frequently as other measures of variability in handling a frequency distribution. (In fact, we have not discussed how it would be found in a frequency distribution.) It is used more often in handling ungrouped data.

The Standard Deviation. σ is used: (1) when the influence of all scores is desired; (2) when it is needed for other statistical formulas and processes; (3) when the greatest "reliability" (explained in Chapter VI) is desired.

The Coefficient of Variation. The coefficient of variation is used in addition to σ in *comparing* the variability of two distributions whose means differ appreciably.

Summary. In this chapter we have discussed the various statistical *measures of variability*, their *computation* from a frequency distribution, and the conditions governing the *choice* of a particular measure of variability. The following exercises are interpretative applications of this material.

EXERCISES

Ex. 17. If you wished to discount the effect of a few very low scores, which measure of variability would you compute in a frequency distribution?

Ex. 18. Which measure of variability is statistically most reliable?

Ex. 19. Which measure of variability is most quickly determined from a frequency distribution?

Ex. 20. Compare the information as to the nature of a distribution given by an average with that given by a measure of variability.

Ex. 21. The σ of the I.Q.'s of a group of children is 10, and the σ of their algebra marks is 8. Would it be correct to say that the group is more variable in intelligence than in achievement in algebra? Explain.

Ex. 22. Find the mean deviation from the mean, the mean deviation from the median, and the standard deviation of the following scores: 10, 9, 9, 8, 7, 6, 4.

Ex. 23. Table 22 is taken from "The Status of Rural Supervisors of Instruction in the United States," by Clyde B. Moore and William E. Cole, *Educational Method*, October, 1932.

TABLE 22

AGE DISTRIBUTION OF RURAL SUPERVISORS

State	Number of supervisors studied	First quartile	Median	Third quartile
Alabama..............	24	30.5	36	45
California..............	32	34.5	39.5	49
New Jersey............	28	34	40	43
Pennsylvania...........	30	40	45	51
Wisconsin.............	43	27	33	39
All states studied (27)...	400	33	39	45

(a) Approximately what percentage of the Alabama supervisors (mentioned in this study) is younger than 30?

(b) What percentage of the Pennsylvania supervisors is over 51?

(c) How many of the New Jersey supervisors are younger than 34?

(d) Which state, as a whole, has the youngest supervisors? Which has the oldest?

(e) In which states is the variability in age of supervisors the greatest?

(f) On the basis of this study what is the average age of a rural supervisor in the United States? Is this the true average age of a rural supervisor? Explain.

Ex. 24. Table 23 is taken from "What Do the Meier-Seashore and the McAdory Art Tests Measure?" by Herbert A. Carroll, *Journal of Educational Research*, May, 1933. The writer of this article tested 152 college students, using the Meier-Seashore Test as a measuring instrument of art-judgment ability. Students were tested before and after taking an art course.

TABLE 23

RESULTS IN THE MEIER-SEASHORE ART-JUDGMENT TEST

Subjects	N	Mean	σ
Art majors			
December, 1929............	49	82.55	5.68
December, 1930............	49	85.53	5.28
Non-art students			
December, 1929............	103	72.92	7.77
December, 1930............	103	74.52	7.17

(a) Which group of students—the art majors, or non-art students—shows greater ability in judging art?

(b) Does the year of art instruction seem to cause an appreciable change in the art-judgment ability of either group? How might you explain this?

(c) Compare the homogeneity of the two groups relative to art-judgment ability. Will the use of σ alone enable you to make the comparison? Explain.

(d) Why do you suppose that the mean and standard deviation were used in this study, rather than other measures of central tendency and variability?

Ex. 25. Table 24 is taken from "The Effect of Practice on the Homogeneity of a Group" by *Robert P. Carroll, Journal of Educational Sociology,* September, 1932.

TABLE 24

CHANGES IN THE COEFFICIENT OF VARIATION
IN SILENT READING

Day of drill	Coefficient of variation
1	26
2	23
3	23
4	20
5	12
6	23
7	22
8	22
9	26
10	18
11	19
12	24
13	26
14	17
15	19
16	21
17	18
18	23
19	14
20	15
21	20
22	15
23	14
24	16
25	16
26	12
27	14
28	15

(a) From these data what conclusion would you draw as to the effect of practice on the homogeneity of the group in achievement in silent reading? Explain.

(*b*) Why do you suppose that the coefficient of variation was used instead of σ in this study?

Ex. 26. The following quotation as well as Tables 25*a–d* are taken from "The Relative Variability of Boys and Girls" by A. Leon Winsor, *Journal of Educational Psychology*, May, 1927:

"In 'Genetic Studies of Genius' (by Terman, L. M., *et. al.*) boys are found far to outnumber girls in the higher I.Q. ranges. This agrees with the supposedly well-established fact of the greater variability of males. . . . The relative variability of males and females has been a subject for many discussions in the past and recognized authorities in the field of psychology have participated on each side of the question."

TABLE 25*a*

SCORES SHOWING THE COMPARATIVE VARIABILITY OF 10-YEAR-OLDS
FOR THE ARMY BETA TEST 2

Sex	Number	Mean	σ	Coefficient of variation
Boys..........	1161	13.12	4.80	0.365
Girls..........	1160	10.06	4.08	0.405

TABLE 25*b*

SCORES SHOWING THE COMPARATIVE VARIABILITY OF 10-YEAR-OLDS
FOR THE ARMY BETA TEST 5

Sex	Number	Mean	σ	Coefficient of variation
Boys..........	1161	24.42	8.15	0.333
Girls..........	1160	27.72	8.70	0.317

TABLE 25*c*

SCORES SHOWING THE COMPARATIVE VARIABILITY IN GEOMETRIC
ABILITIES

Exercise 9

Sex	Number	Mean	σ	Coefficient of variation
Males.........	1289	5.9	2.6	0.44
Females.......	1504	4.7	2.3	0.51

Exercise 11

Males.........	924	8.3	3.1	0.37
Females.......	921	7.3	3.5	0.48

TABLE 25d

SCORES SHOWING THE COMPARATIVE VARIABILITY IN PERFORMANCE
ON THE NATIONAL INTELLIGENCE TESTS

Age	Sex	Number	Mean	σ	Coefficient of variation
10	Male..........	95	148.5	52	0.35
10	Female........	97	158.1	44.8	0.28
11	Male..........	99	171.9	51	0.29
11	Female........	98	190	54	0.28

(a) Compare mean achievement of 10-year-old boys and girls on Army Beta Test 2; on Army Beta Test 5. Compare the variabilities on the two tests. Would the results indicate greater variability on the part of 10-year-old boys?

(b) Compare variabilities for boys and girls in Geometry Exercise 9; in Geometry Exercise 11. If these results are *typical* for all exercises, would you say that boys are more variable than girls in geometric ability?

(c) Compare the variability of 10-year-old boys and girls in the National Intelligence Tests. Would you expect the highest intelligence scores to be found among the boys or the girls? Explain.

(d) Answer the same questions as in (c) for 11-year-old boys and girls.

(e) If Tables 25a–d are *typical* of the data available on the subject of the relative variability of boys and girls, do they indicate greater variability on the part of the males? If the tables are typical, would you expect boys "far to outnumber girls in the higher I.Q. ranges"? Would you expect to find more male than female geniuses?

Ex. 27. Tables 26a and b are taken from "Improving and Evaluating the Efficiency of College Instruction" by C. H. Smeltzer, *Journal of Educational Psychology*, April, 1933. This study describes an experiment with a group of college students who were studying educational psychology. "Control" sections and "experimental" sections were subjected to somewhat different procedures and the results studied. Data given here are for the winter quarter students.

TABLE 26a

STATISTICAL CHARACTERISTICS OF THE INTELLIGENCE
PERCENTILES FOR THE WINTER QUARTER

	Experimental	Control
90th percentile.............	97.2	96.6
Q_3........................	86.8	88.1
Median....................	56.9	69.8
Q_1........................	37.7	41
10th percentile.............	27.6	32

TABLE 26b

STATISTICAL CHARACTERISTICS OF THE PRE AND END TEST SCORES FOR EXPERI-
MENTAL AND CONTROL SECTIONS FOR THE WINTER QUARTER

	Pre Test		End Test	
	Experimental	Control	Experimental	Control
90th percentile......	158	156.2	262.8	257
Q_3.................	129.4	137	245	241
Median.............	117.3	120	230.6	222
Q_1.................	93.3	93.8	215.5	195
10th percentile......	74.3	77	202.3	172
Mean..............	114.8	116.8	231.1	216.8

(a) Compare the experimental and control groups in median intelligence; in variability. Compare the two groups in intelligence at all the percentile points for which data are given.

(b) Compare the two groups in the pre-test with respect to central tendency and variability. Compare them at all percentile points.

(c) Answer the same questions as in (b) for the end test.

(d) On the basis of your answers to (a), (b), and (c) what conclusion would you draw as to the nature of the instruction in experimental and control groups?

Ex. 28. From an inspection of the following table answer the following questions:

(a) In this particular group, what seems to be the effect of mathematical training on performance in the Carter test? Explain your answer.

(b) Would you come to any general conclusion as to the value of mathematical training as a preparation for the study of physics? Explain.

(c) What explanation can you offer of the apparent inconsistency shown by the decrease in mean between the second and third semesters and the decrease in both the median and the mean between the seventh and eighth semesters?

(d) Find the semi-interquartile range for students with two semesters' training in mathematics.

(e) Which group of students has the least homogeneous grouping?

(f) How many students in the eight-semester group scored higher than 58?

TABLE 27*

THE RELATION BETWEEN MATHEMATICS TRAINING AND PERFORMANCE ON THE
CARTER TEST FOR MATHEMATICAL CONCEPTS IN HIGH-SCHOOL PHYSICS

Semesters' training in mathematics	Mean	Performance in the Carter test				
		Median	Q_1	Q_3	Number
2......................	45.2	44.8	40.7	48.7	40
3......................	45.1	45.0	38.0	54.5	16
4......................	46.8	48.8	42.5	53.2	148
5......................	49.0	50.8	42.8	56.4	58
6......................	51.4	52.3	46.9	57.6	79
7......................	54.8	56.6	52.6	59.6	49
8......................	53.3	56.0	51.0	58.0	12
9......................	59.5	59.5			2

* Same source as Table 16.

Ex. 29. The following table is taken from "A Test of Scientific Aptitude" by D. L. Zyve, *Journal of Educational Psychology*, November, 1927. It gives the results of a test devised by the author as a measure of scientific aptitude.

TABLE 28

RESULTS ON TSA OF A GROUP OF STANFORD UNIVERSITY FACULTY AND STUDENTS

No.	Group	Minimum score	Maximum score	Mean	Standard deviation
246	Unselected freshmen.......	47	166	105	28.3
50	Research.................	45	166	134	27.3
21	Science faculty............	133	177	153	13
14	Non-science faculty........	95	167	118	24
79	Science freshmen..........	45	156	113	27.9
47	Seniors and graduates—non-science.................	30	155	90	29.3

(*a*) Do the achievements of the groups as a whole conform with the results you would naturally expect? Explain.

(*b*) Which group is least homogeneous with respect to scientific aptitude? Explain.

(*c*) For which group do you consider the results most reliable? Explain.

(*d*) Examine the range and standard deviation for the science faculty. Is there anything unusual about these figures? What do they indicate as to the nature of the test?

(*e*) Judging from these results, do you think this a good test of scientific aptitude?

(*f*) Write a set of classes which you would consider appropriate for grouping the freshmen scores into a frequency distribution.

Ex. 30. Mark the following + or —:

( ) 1. Mean deviation from the mean is an average.

( ) 2. In using Q the effect of extreme scores is discounted.

( ) 3. A shortened method of finding the mean cannot be applied to ungrouped scores.

( ) 4. A frequency polygon gives an exact graphic representation of a frequency distribution.

( ) 5. In any frequency distribution, the quartiles are at equal numerical distances from the median.

( ) 6. A certain group is given an intelligence test and a mathematics achievement test. For the intelligence test, $Q = 10$. For the mathematics test, $Q = 14$. Hence the group is more homogeneous in intelligence than in mathematical ability.

( ) 7. The ninth decile is exceeded by 90 per cent of the scores in a distribution.

( ) 8. In two sets of scores with equal sigmas, the set with the greater mean is less variable.

( ) 9. If the five lowest scores in a set are decreased, the standard deviation will be increased.

( ) 10. The mean is the best measure of central tendency for the purpose of drawing general conclusions.

( ) 11. Most educational data are treated in the form of ungrouped series.

( ) 12. If two groups have equal Q's, they are equally variable.

( ) 13. For the purpose of drawing general conclusions, the standard deviation is a better measure of variability than the semi-interquartile range.

( ) 14. The mean should be used as a measure of central tendency in a distribution, if it is desired to discount the effect of a few very high scores.

( ) 15. In grouping 400 scores which range from 10 to 95, a class interval of 10 would be a good choice.

( ) 16. In a frequency distribution with 100 cases, a class interval of 5, and a range of 90, the 10 lowest cases are raised 10 per cent each. The standard deviation will be unaffected.

Ex. 31. Bring in illustrative material from educational periodicals showing the use of the various measures of variability in statistical studies.

CHAPTER IV

GRAPHS

The Bar Graph. Table 29 is taken from the April issue of the *Educational Bulletin* of the State of New Jersey Department of

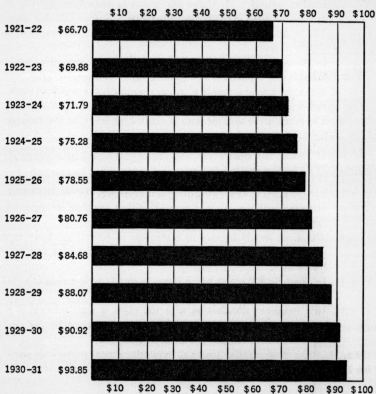

FIG. 9.—Bar Graph of Total Instructional Costs in New Jersey from 1921–2 to 1930–1

Public Instruction. Fig. 9 is taken from the same pamphlet. It is a *bar graph* of the data in the last column of that table. Any one will concede that the *graphic* representation tells the tale of the increasing cost of education much more vividly than the column of figures in the table. It is for this reason that graphic methods are important in all statistical work.

In the figure $\frac{1}{32}$ inch is taken to represent \$1.00. Hence $\frac{10}{32}$ or $\frac{5}{16}$ inch represents \$10.00. The vertical lines in the diagram are $\frac{5}{16}$ inch apart, and the distance between them represents \$10.00.

The expenditure for 1921–2 is \$66.70. Thus the bar for this year will cover $\frac{66.70}{10} = 6.67$ or approximately 6.7 spaces.

For 1922–3, $\frac{69.88}{10} = 6.988 = 7$ spaces, approximately, etc.

Bar graphs are generally drawn on cross-section paper, for, as this paper is ruled in inches or centimeters and fractional parts of these units, its use is an aid to accuracy and saves time.

In a bar graph the bars may also be constructed in a vertical position. The histogram of Chapter I is a type of bar graph. In it, the bars are in a vertical position with no space between

TABLE 29

AVERAGE INSTRUCTIONAL COSTS IN DAY SCHOOLS PER PUPIL IN AVERAGE DAILY ATTENDANCE FOR THE STATE IN THE SCHOOL YEARS 1921–2 TO AND INCLUDING 1930–31

Year	Supervision	Teachers' salaries	Textbooks	Supplies	Other instructional items	Total instructional costs
1921–22........	\$5.24	\$56.91	\$1.75	\$2.80	\$ *	\$66.70
1922–23........	5.73	59.56	1.80	2.79	*	69.88
1923–24........	5.62	61.53	1.87	2.77	*	71.79
1924–25........	6.64	63.67	2.08	2.77	0.12	75.28
1925–26........	7.28	66.30	1.89	2.82	0.26	78.55
1926–27........	7.46	68.27	1.96	2.81	0.26	80.76
1927–28........	7.99	71.25	2.07	3.11	0.26	84.68
1928–29........	8.36	74.20	2.09	3.16	0.26	88.07
1929–30........	8.83	76.34	2.14	3.39	0.22	90.92
1930–31........	9.12	79.02	2.11	3.41	0.19	93.85

* Other instructional expenditures in 1921–2, 1922–3, and 1923–4 included under Supplies.

them. In most bar graphs, however, it is customary to leave a space between the bars. The bars are constructed to have the same width, and usually the space between them is made equal to this width.

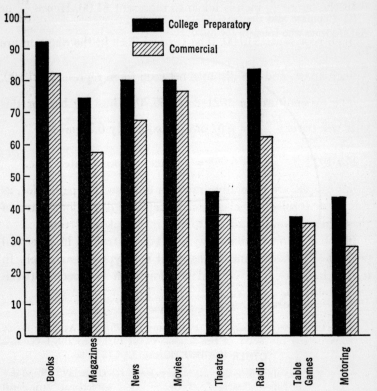

Fig. 10.—Per cent of students giving out-of-school time to cultural recreation activities*

*From "Out-of-School Activities of High School Girls," by Ada E. Orr and Francis J. Brown—Journal of Educational Sociology, Jan. 1932.

EXERCISES

Ex. 1. Make a bar graph using the data in Table 29 to show the cost of supervision per pupil for the school years 1921–2 to and including 1930–31.

Ex. 2. Make a vertical bar graph, using data in the same table, to show the cost of teachers' salaries per pupil for the years 1921–2 to and including 1930–31.

Ex. 3. Fig. 10 shows a *double bar* graph. It represents the results of a questionnaire given to 200 girls in the ninth and tenth grades in the high school, 100 of whom were college-preparatory and 100 commercial students.

(*a*) From the graph, compare the time spent outside of school on cultural activities by college-preparatory students with that spent by commercial students.

(*b*) Compare also the percentages of college-preparatory and commercial students who listen to the radio. How might this be accounted for?

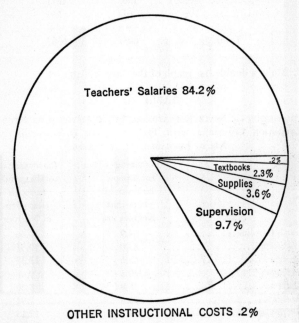

OTHER INSTRUCTIONAL COSTS .2%

FIG. 11.—Instructional costs in New Jersey schools for 1930–1

(*c*) Compare percentages for the movies.

(*d*) What is the cultural activity in which most students of both types engage?

(*e*) What is the cultural activity in which fewest college-preparatory students engage? Explain.

(*f*) What is the cultural activity in which fewest commercial students engage? Explain.

(*g*) Compare the percentage of college-preparatory students who read magazines with those who go to the movies. Do the same for the commercial students.

Ex. 4. The following table furnishes a comparison of mid-term and final marks given to 6087 students in a certain high school. Make a double-bar graph to represent it.

TABLE 30

Mark	Mid-term	Final
A	512	572
B	1293	1229
C	1946	1896
D	1663	1821
E	673	569
Total	6087	6087

Ex. 5. Make a double-bar graph of the data of Table 31.

TABLE 31*

PROPORTION OF STATE EDUCATIONAL FUNDS DEVOTED TO NEGRO EDUCATION COMPARED WITH PROPORTIONATE DISTRIBUTION OF NEGRO EDUCABLES IN 17 STATES

State	Percentage of total population 6–13 years that Negroes are	Percentage of total expenditures for education of Negroes
South Carolina	54.9	10.66
Mississippi	53.0	10.51
Georgia	43.5	13.33
Louisiana	39.3	9.98
Alabama	38.9	8.40
Florida	36.9	7.91
North Carolina	31.5	12.13
Virginia	31.3	11.09
Arkansas	35.9	15.99
Tennessee	22.9	11.93
Maryland	17.8	9.67
Texas	16.2	12.00
Delaware	14.4	13.70
Kentucky	8.2	8.02
Oklahoma	7.2	4.73
West Virginia	4.7	4.65
Missouri	7.1	3.15

* Taken from the U. S. Department of Interior Bulletin 20, 1931, Biennial Survey of Education in the United States, 1928–30.

Circle Graph. Fig. 11 illustrates a circle or "pie" graph of the data in the last horizontal line of Table 29. A graph of this type is used to illustrate the relative magnitude of the parts into which a whole quantity is divided. The figure was constructed as follows:

The cost of each item—supervision, teachers' salaries, etc.—was divided by the total cost in order to find what fraction of the total cost it was. Thus,

$$Supervision = \frac{9.12}{93.85} = 9.7\%$$

Then, since there are 360 degrees in the circumference of a circle:

$$9.7\% \text{ of } 360° = 34.9°$$

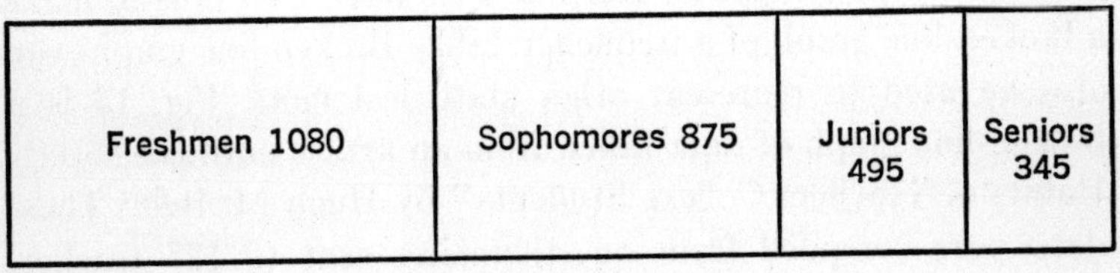

Freshmen 1080	Sophomores 875	Juniors 495	Seniors 345

FIG. 12.—Divided-bar graph

Next, the following table was constructed. The student can fill in the missing details:

Items	Cost	Percentage of total cost	Angle
Supervision................	$9.12	9.7	34.9°
Teachers' salaries..........			
Textbooks................			
Supplies...................			

Next, by the use of a protractor, the angles were laid off at the center of the circle.

Ex. 6. Using the data of Table 29 make a circle graph showing the costs for the various items of expenditure in the year 1929–30.

Ex. 7. Using Table 29 make a circle graph of the expenditures for the year 1928–9.

Ex. 8. In a certain high school there are 1080 freshmen, 875 sophomores, 495 juniors, 345 seniors. Make a "pie" graph to illustrate these facts.

Divided-Bar Graph. Fig. 12 is a divided-bar graph illustrating the facts of Ex. 8.

Ex. 9. Make a divided-bar graph to show the costs for various items in the year 1929–30, using Table 29.

Ex. 10. A student spends his day as follows:

> School.................................... 6 hours
> Sleep..................................... 8 hours
> Study..................................... 4 hours
> Recreation................................ 2 hours
> Miscellaneous............................. 4 hours
> (Meals, traveling to school and back, etc.)

Represent these data by a divided-bar graph. Why is this form of representation far more convenient, in this instance, than a circle graph?

Broken-Line Graph. In Chapter I we have seen how to make a broken-line graph of a frequency table. Broken-line graphs can also be used to represent other statistical facts. Fig. 13 is a broken-line graph of data taken from an article entitled "Study Habits of Teachers College Students" by Hugh M. Bell.[1] These data were compiled from questionnaires sent to 127 teachers college students and are given in Table 32.

TABLE 32

Day of week	Daily average number of minutes spent on study
Sunday.....................	128
Monday....................	140
Tuesday...................	168
Wednesday.................	148
Thursday..................	140
Friday....................	92
Saturday..................	116

Ex. 11. Answer the following questions, using Fig. 13:

(a) On what day of the week do these students study the most? the least? How would you account for this?

[1] *Journal of Educational Psychology*, October, 1931.

(b) How much time do the students give to study, on the average, on Saturday?

(c) On what days of the week does the "average" student give approximately equal amounts of time to study?

(d) How much more time, on the average, is spent on studies on Tuesday than on Sunday?

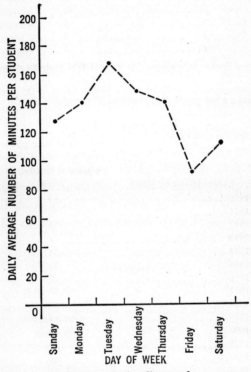

Fig. 13.—Broken-line graph

Ex. 12. A student handed in algebra papers on ten successive days and received the following grades (on a scale of 10): 5, 6, 7½, 8½, 7, 6, 7½, 8, 8, 10. Make a broken-line graph of his progress. On the same graph plot the marks of a second student: 4, 5, 5, 6, 6½, 7, 6, 5, 7, 7.

Ex. 13. Make a broken-line graph of the last column of Table 29 (i.e., the same data which are plotted as a bar graph in Fig. 9).

Ex. 14. Make a broken-line graph to represent Table 33, which contains data on the teaching of science in 182 New Jersey schools.

TABLE 33*

Number of sciences offered	Number of schools
0	1
1	21
2	15
3	38
4	87
5	12
6	5
7	1
8	1

* "Preparation of Teachers in New Jersey" by Rufus D. Reed in *Journal of Chemical Education*, February, 1932.

Ex. 15. Make a bar graph and a broken-line graph of the data of Table 34.

TABLE 34**

Class (given by year)	Number of New Jersey State Teachers College graduates teaching in 1930
1910	12
1911	20
1912	23
1913	38
1914	34
1915	46
1916	37
1917	55
1918	65
1919	53
1920	46
1921	59
1922	44
1923	64
1924	75
1925	60
1926	104
1927	165
1928	135
1929	98

** From the 1930–31 Catalogue of the New Jersey State Teachers College at Montclair.

Curved-Line Graph. When facts are so related to each other that they represent a gradual or *continuous* change, they are usually represented by a *curved-line* graph.

Fig. 14 illustrates such a graph. A curved-line graph is used, since *weight* changes continuously.

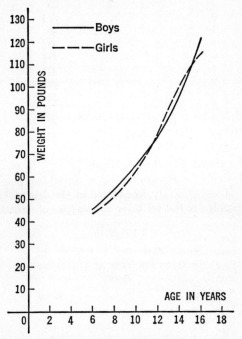

FIG. 14.—Curved-line graph

Broken-line graphs, on the other hand, are used to represent sudden changes.

Ex. 16. From the graph in Fig. 14, answer the following:

(*a*) At what age is the difference between the average weights of boys and girls the greatest?

(*b*) At what age is their average weight approximately the same?

(*c*) Find approximately the average weight of 7-year-old boys; of 13-year-old girls.

Ex. 17. Draw a curved-line graph of the data in Table 35. Such a curve is called a *growth curve*. Determine from the graph the approximate height of the boy at age 3 years 6 months; at 8 years 8 months.

TABLE 35

THE HEIGHT OF A CERTAIN BOY AT EACH
AGE FROM BIRTH TO 12 YEARS

Age in years	Height in inches
0	22
1	$28\frac{1}{2}$
2	33
3	$36\frac{3}{4}$
4	40
5	$42\frac{3}{4}$
6	$45\frac{1}{4}$
7	$47\frac{1}{2}$
8	$49\frac{1}{2}$
9	52
10	$53\frac{1}{2}$
11	55
12	57

Ex. 18. Like growth in weight or height, growth in mental ability is gradual, and should be represented by a curved-line graph. Draw the growth curve of mental ability represented by the data of Table 36. (The scores in an intelligence test are taken as measures of mental ability.)

TABLE 36

SCORES MADE BY A BOY IN AN
INTELLIGENCE TEST AT DIFFERENT
AGES

Age	Score
9	15
10	23
11	27
12	34
13	41
14	48
15	53
16	56
17	58
18	58

From the graph describe the nature of the boy's mental growth from ages 11 to 14; after 14.

The Mathematical Graph. The types of graphs which have been treated thus far may all be classified under the general heading of *statistical graphs*. In contrast to these we shall now treat the *mathematical graph*, which is also of importance in statistical work.

The principles involved in plotting a mathematical graph are very similar to those used in the statistical graph, and are doubtless familiar to the reader. Nevertheless we shall state them briefly here.

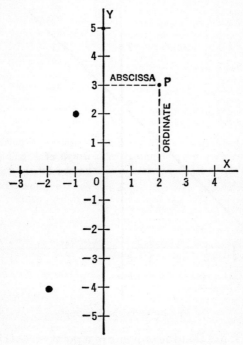

Fig. 15.—Coordinate axes

In Fig. 15, two straight lines OX and OY meet at right angles. These lines are termed the x axis and the y axis respectively, or the axis of *abscissas* and axis of *ordinates* respectively. The point O is called the *origin*. The distance of a point P from the y axis is known as the x coordinate, or *abscissa*; and the distance from the x axis is known as the y coordinate, or *ordinate*. Every point has thus two coordinates. The point P in Fig. 15 has the coordinates (2, 3).

The points $(-1, 2)$, $(-2, -4)$, $(0, 5)$, $(-3, 0)$ have also been located in the figure.

Ex. 19. Plot two coordinate axes and locate the following points: $(3, 5)$, $(-2, -2)$, $(0, -3)$, $(-2, 0)$, $(3, -4)$, $(-4, 7)$.

The Linear Equation. An equation like $y = x + 5$ represents a relation between the two coordinates of a point. In this case

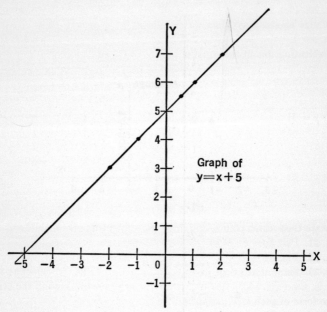

Graph of
$y = x + 5$

FIG. 16.—Straight-line graph

the relation states that the ordinate of a point exceeds its abscissa by 5. There are infinitely many points which satisfy this condition, for example: $(1, 6)$, $(2, 7)$, $(0, 5)$, $(-1, 4)$, $(-2, 3)$, $(\frac{1}{2}, 5\frac{1}{2})$, etc.

The graphic picture of an equation consists of all points whose coordinates satisfy the conditions of the equation. Fig. 16 gives the picture of $y = x + 5$. The points listed above have been plotted. They seem to lie in a straight line. It can be proved mathematically that this is the case, and hence the graph of $y = x + 5$ is a straight line.

In fact, it can be proved that *every equation of the first degree in* x *and* y *represents a straight line.* Such equations are termed *linear*, for this reason.

Hence, in order to plot a linear equation, only two points need be located, for two points determine a straight line. It is better, of course, to plot three points, so that the position of the third point may serve as a check.

Ex. 20. Plot $2y + 3x = 5$.
We may choose any values we wish for x.
Let $x = 1$.
Substituting this in the equation:

$$2y + 3 = 5$$
$$2y = 2$$
$$y = 1$$

Let $x = 3$:

$$2y + 9 = 5$$
$$2y = -4$$
$$y = -2$$

x	y
1	1
3	-2
5	-5

Let $x = 5$:

$$2y + 15 = 5$$
$$2y = -10$$
$$y = -5$$

Locate these three points, and draw the straight line through them.

Ex. 21. Plot $3y - 5x = 10$.

Ex. 22. Plot $2y = 5x$.

Ex. 23. Show that every linear equation which lacks the constant term (that is, the term which does not involve x or y) passes through the origin.

The form of such an equation will be

$$ay = bx$$

Now the coordinates of the origin are $(0, 0)$.
Substituting these, we have:

$$a \cdot 0 = b \cdot 0$$
$$0 = 0$$

and hence, since the coordinates of the origin satisfy this equation, this point lies on the line represented by $ay = bx$.

Ex. 24. Plot $4x - 5y - 2 = 0$.

Ex. 25. Plot $x = 5$.
Let $x = 5$. $y =$ anything, since it is not mentioned in the equation.

x	y
5	0
5	1
5	2

Ex. 26. Plot $y = 2$.

Let $x = 0$.

    $y = 2$ according to the equation.

x	y
0	2
1	2
2	2

Let $x = 1$

    $y = 2$, etc.

Ex. 27. Plot $x = -3$.

Ex. 28. Plot $y = -4$.

Ex. 29. What is the picture of $x = a$? (a is any constant). What is the picture of $y = b$?

Ex. 30. What line is represented by $x = 0$? by $y = 0$?

Equations of Degree Higher Than the First.
An equation involving powers of x or y higher than the first degree has as its graph some type of curve.

Ex. 31. Plot $y = x^2 + x - 6$.

To plot a non-linear relationship, it is well to choose a few negative and a few positive values of x and then to find the corresponding values of y. After plotting these points and joining them by a smooth curve, the form of this curve will indicate whether it is necessary to plot more points.

In this case, let us choose values of x from -3 to $+3$.

If $x = -3$ $y = 9 - 3 - 6 = 0$, etc.

Fill in the necessary values of y.

x	y
-3	0
-2	
-1	
0	
1	
2	
3	
-4	

These points have been plotted in Fig. 17 and have been joined by a smooth curve. The figure indicates the need of obtaining one more point to the left of $(-3, 0)$. Hence,

$$x = -4$$
$$y = 6$$

has been added.

Ex. 32. Plot $y = 2x^2 - x - 1$

    Use 4 spaces $= 1$ on the x axis.

        1 space $= 1$ on the y axis.

Ex. 33. Plot $y = x^2 + x + 1$
Ex. 34. Plot $y = x^2 - 4x + 4$
Ex. 35. Plot $y = x^3$
Ex. 36. Plot $y = x^3 - 7x - 6$

Graphic Treatment of Percentiles. In Chapter II the meaning and computation of percentiles have been introduced inciden-

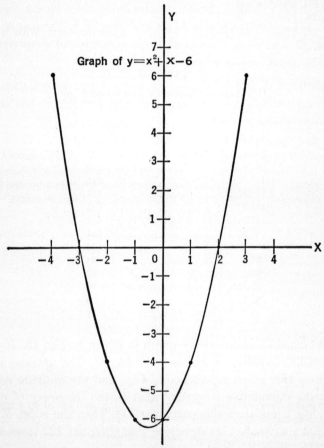

FIG. 17.—Graph of a parabola

tally. Since the use of percentiles in connection with educational tests is becoming increasingly important, we shall give a more detailed treatment of this topic.

Cumulative Frequency Graph. Let us see how percentiles may be determined *graphically*. The data of Table 8 have been re-grouped in Table 37 in the form of a *cumulative frequency distribution*. The frequency of I.Q.'s less than 77.5 is 1, the number of cases in the lowest class of Table 8. Adding the frequencies in the two lowest classes of Table 8, $1 + 5 = 6$ cases with I.Q.'s less than 82.5. Adding the frequencies in the three lowest classes, $1 + 5 + 14 = 20$ cases with I.Q.'s less than 87.5. The rest of the entries in the second column of Table 37 are found similarly.

TABLE 37

CUMULATIVE FREQUENCY DISTRIBUTION OF
TABLE 8

I.Q.	Frequency less than given I.Q.
137.5	221
132.5	219
127.5	218
122.5	211
117.5	196
112.5	181
107.5	154
102.5	122
97.5	83
92.5	47
87.5	20
82.5	6
77.5	1

The cumulative frequency graph is shown in Fig. 18. It is a broken-line graph of the data in Table 37. The abscissa of a point on this graph represents an I.Q., and the ordinate represents the cumulative frequency, that is, the frequency of cases with I.Q.'s less than this particular I.Q. Thus the point P has coordinates (102.5, 122) signifying that there are 122 cases with I.Q.'s less than 102.5.

Let us see how to find an approximate value of the 20th percentile from this graph

$$20\% \text{ of } 221 = \frac{1}{5} \times 221 = 44.2$$

The 20th percentile is thus the 44.2th case. We see from the graph that the point R, with ordinate 44.2 approximately, has

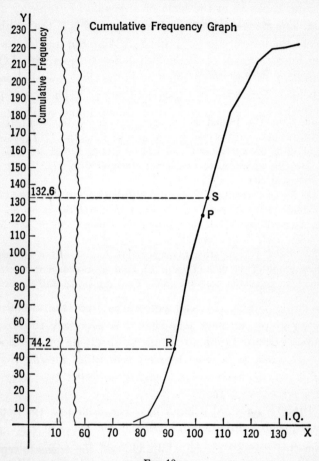

FIG. 18

an abscissa = 92 approximately. Hence the 20th percentile is approximately 92. Similarly, for the 60th percentile:

$$60\% \text{ of } 221 = \frac{3}{5} \times 221 = 132.6$$

The point S, with ordinate = 132.6 approximately, has 104 as abscissa. Hence, the 60th percentile is approximately 104.

Applying the method of Chapter II for finding percentiles, we have, using Table 8,

$$20\text{th percentile} = 87.5 + \frac{24.2}{27} \times 5$$

$$= 87.5 + 4.5 = 92.0$$

$$60\text{th percentile} = 102.5 + \frac{10.6}{32} \times 5$$

$$= 102.5 + 1.7 = 104.2$$

Ex. 37. From Fig. 18 find the approximate value of the 80th percentile of the distribution represented by the graph. Find the 45th percentile. Check by using the method of Chapter II for finding percentiles. From the graph, find the approximate number of students with I.Q.'s lower than 100; lower than 110.

Ex. 38. Make a cumulative frequency distribution and a cumulative frequency graph of the data of Table 13. From the graph determine approximately the 30th percentile, Q_1, Q_3, and the median. About how many students had scores lower than 30?

Ex. 39. Make a cumulative frequency distribution and a cumulative frequency graph of the data of Table 10. Find approximate values of the 40th and 90th percentiles from the graph. Find also Q_1, Q_3, and the median.

Percentile Graph. To read percentiles from the cumulative frequency graph, we have seen that it is necessary to do some preliminary computation to obtain the ordinate of the desired point. In order to be able to read percentiles *directly* from a graph, it is convenient to use a slightly different type of graph, called a *percentile graph*.

In Table 38, a third column has been added to the data of Table 37. This third column gives the *percentage* of cases with I.Q.'s less than a given I.Q. Thus, since all the I.Q.'s fall below 137.5, the first entry in the third column is 100. Since 219 I.Q.'s fall below 132.5, $\frac{219}{221} = 99.1$ per cent of the I.Q.'s fall below 132.5, and 99.1 is the second entry in the third column. For the third entry, we have $\frac{218}{221} = 98.6$ per cent. The remainder of the third column is obtained in a similar manner.

In Fig. 19, the data of Table 38 have been plotted as a *percentile graph*. The ordinate of each point is an I.Q., and the abscissa is the percentage of cases with I.Q.'s below this particular I.Q. Thus, P has the coordinates (55.2, 102.5) which signify that 55.2 per cent of the I.Q.'s fall below 102.5, or that the 55.2th percentile is 102.5. In Table 38, the third column is the table of abscissas, and the first column is the table of ordinates.

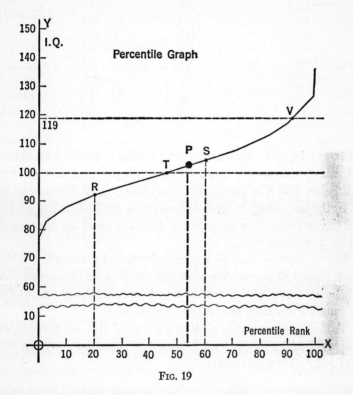

FIG. 19

We can now see how to read percentiles directly from this graph. To find the 20th percentile we locate the point R with abscissa 20. Its ordinate is 92, which is the approximate value of the 20th percentile. This is the same as the result obtained above from the cumulative frequency graph.

To find the 60th percentile we locate S with abscissa 60. Its ordinate is 104, which is the value of the 60th percentile.

The *percentile rank* of a score is defined as the *percentage of cases below this score*. Let us find the percentile rank of an I.Q.

TABLE 38

I.Q.	Cumulative frequency	Percentage frequency less than given I.Q.
137.5..............	221	100.0
132.5..............	219	99.1
127.5..............	218	98.6
122.5..............	211	95.5
117.5..............	196	88.7
112.5..............	181	81.9
107.5..............	154	69.7
102.5..............	122	55.2
97.5..............	83	37.6
92.5..............	47	21.3
87.5..............	20	9.0
82.5..............	6	2.7
77.5..............	1	0.5

of 100 in Fig. 19. We locate T with ordinate 100. Its abscissa is 46, which means that approximately 46 per cent of the I.Q.'s fall below 100. The percentile rank of an I.Q. of 100 is thus 46.

In the same way, to find the percentile rank of an I.Q. of 119, we locate point V with ordinate 119, and read its abscissa 91 as the percentile rank.

Let us see how to find a percentile rank by *numerical* rather than graphical means. We shall use the process of *interpolation*, which we have used previously in connection with the finding of square roots from the table of square roots.

To find the percentile rank of an I.Q. of 100, we first inspect Table 38 and note that an I.Q. of 100 is located between 97.5 and 102.5. Thus we have:

$$5\begin{bmatrix} 102.5 & 55.2 \\ 2.5\begin{bmatrix}100 \\ 97.5\end{bmatrix} & \begin{matrix}? \\ 37.6\end{matrix}\Big]? \end{bmatrix}17.6$$

I.Q.   Percentile rank

In going from 97.5 to 100, the change in I.Q. is 2.5. The whole change in I.Q. from 97.5 to 102.5 is 5. Hence, we have:

$$\frac{2.5}{5} = \frac{25}{50} = \frac{1}{2} \text{ of the total change}$$

Assuming that changes in percentile rank are proportional to changes in I.Q., the corresponding change in percentile rank is also equal to $\frac{1}{2}$ of the total change.

$$\frac{1}{2} \times 17.6 = 8.8 = \text{change in percentile rank}$$

Hence the percentile rank is

$$37.6 + 8.8 = 46.4$$

Again, to find the percentile rank of an I.Q. of 119, we have:

$$5\begin{bmatrix} \text{I.Q.} \\ 122.5 \\ 1.5\begin{bmatrix} 119 \\ 117.5 \end{bmatrix} \end{bmatrix} \quad \begin{bmatrix} \text{Percentile rank} \\ 95.5 \\ ? \\ 88.7 \end{bmatrix}? \Big] 6.8$$

The change in I.Q. is

$$\frac{1.5}{5} = \frac{15}{50} = \frac{3}{10} \text{ of the total change}$$

Hence, for the percentile rank the total change is

$$\frac{3}{10} \times 6.8 = 2.04$$

Hence the percentile rank is

$$88.7 + 2.04 = 90.74 = 90.7 \text{ (to the nearest tenth)}$$

For a geometric proof of the validity of the interpolation, see Fig. 20. In this figure, we have, by *similar triangles*:

$$\frac{x}{17.6} = \frac{2.5}{5}$$

$$\frac{x}{17.6} = \frac{1}{2}$$

$$x = \frac{1}{2} \cdot (17.6) = 8.8$$

(Note that this is exactly the same computation as we have performed above.)

$$\text{Percentile rank of } 100 = 37.6 + 8.8 = 46.4$$

Similarly, to find the percentile rank of an I.Q. of 119, we use Fig. 21. By similar triangles:

$$\frac{x}{6.8} = \frac{1.5}{5} = \frac{3}{10}$$

$$x = \frac{3}{10} \cdot (6.8) = 2.04$$

(Note again that this is exactly the same computation as we have performed above.)

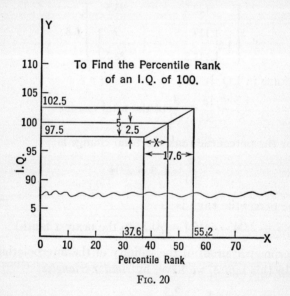

Fig. 20

Percentile rank of $119 = 88.7 + 2.04 = 90.74 = 90.7$ (to the nearest tenth).

Ex. 40. Fill in the following table for the data of Table 13:

Score	Percentage of cases less than given score

Plot the percentile graph, and from it determine the 35th percentile, the 65th percentile, the median, Q_1, and Q_3. From the graph find the percentile rank of a score of 21; of a score of 35. Find these ranks by the numerical method also.

Ex. 41. Using the data of Table 10, prepare a table suitable for the plotting of a percentile graph (that is, one similar to the table used in the previous example). Plot the percentile graph. From this graph determine

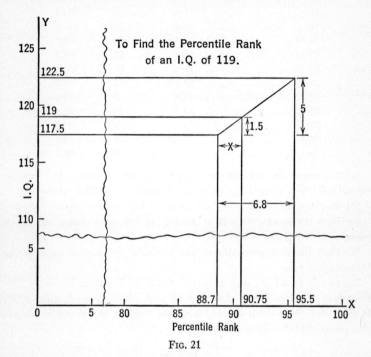

FIG. 21

the median and the 80th percentile. Determine graphically and numerically the percentile rank of a score of 143; of a score of 78.

Ex. 42. Using the data of Table 6, prepare a table suitable for the plotting of a percentile graph. Plot this graph, and from it determine the 20th percentile, Q_1, and Q_3. Determine graphically and numerically the percentile ranks of scores of 95, 200, and 270 respectively.

Summary. In this chapter we have discussed *graphic methods*, and, in particular, have stressed the use of *cumulative frequency* and *percentile* graphs. Further applications follow.

Ex. 43. Table 39 is taken from "A Study of Test Results at the Third and Fifth Grade Levels" by Dallas Eyre Buzby, *The Psychological Clinic*, March, 1931.

TABLE 39

DECILE TABLE FOR FIFTH-GRADE LEVEL
GROUP III

Chronological age	Mental age	Percentile rank	I.Q.
11	15–6	100	146.4
11	12–8	90	117.1
10–11	11–10	80	109.9
10–11	11–4	70	106.2
10–10	11–1	60	103.1
10–9	10–10	50	100.7
10–8	10–8	40	98.4
10–8	10–5	30	96.9
10–7	10–2	20	95.2
10–7	9–10	10	89.8
10–7	8–9	0	80.1

(a) What was the average chronological age in this group, the average mental age, the average I.Q.? (Is this average mean, median, or mode?)

(b) Find the semi-interquartile range of the I.Q.'s and of the mental ages.

(c) Find the percentile rank of an I.Q. of 100, of a mental age of 10 years, of a mental age of 13 years.

(d) Find the 15th percentile of the I.Q.'s, of the mental ages, of the chronological ages.

Ex. 44. Table 40 is taken from "A Study of Behavior Problems" by Georgiana S. Mendenhall, *The Psychological Clinic*, June–August, 1932. It gives data concerning the I.Q.'s of 500 children in the public schools who presented behavior problems.

TABLE 40

PERCENTILES FOR THE DISTRIBUTION OF I.Q.'S
OF BEHAVIOR-PROBLEM CHILDREN

	I.Q.	
Percentile	Boys	Girls
100	127.5	112.5
90	101.8	96.9
80	94.3	91.6
70	89.3	88.4
60	85.4	84.0
50	81.8	78.1
40	78.5	74.7
30	74.5	71.5
20	69.3	68.1
10	65.7	62.5

(a) What is the median I.Q. of the boys? of the girls?

(b) Approximately what median I.Q. would you expect in a group of boys and girls selected at random from *regular* students?

(c) Then how does the intelligence of this group of behavior-problem children compare, as a whole, with that of an unselected group of children?

(d) Find the percentile rank of an I.Q. of 100 in the boys' group; in the girls' group.

(e) Approximately what percentage of the boys is inferior in intelligence to the median of an unselected group? what percentage of the girls?

(f) Compare the boys' group with the girls' group at the various percentile points.

(g) Compare the variability of the two groups.

Ex. 45. Table 41 is taken from "What Do Children Come to the Psychological Clinic For?" by Miles Murphy, *The Psychological Clinic*, March, 1930.

(a) Compare the median normal boy and the median clinic boy. Do the same for girls.

(b) Compare normal and clinic groups as to variability.

(c) What percentage of the clinic cases exceed the highest normal I.Q. (1) among the boys? (2) among the girls?

(d) What percentage of the clinic cases fall below the lowest normal I.Q. (1) among the boys? (2) among the girls?

(e) What percentage of the clinic cases fall outside the normal range (1) among the boys? (2) among the girls?

(f) Summarize the differences in the character of the intelligence of normal children and clinic cases.

TABLE 41

INTELLIGENCE QUOTIENTS FOR NORMAL CHILDREN AND CLINIC CASES (1929)

	Males		Females	
Percentile	Normal	Clinic cases	Normal	Clinic cases
100.....................	153	172	152	163
90.....................	123	130	120	134
80.....................	116	122	113	123
70.....................	111	113	108	115
60.....................	107	105	104	107
50.....................	103	98	100	93
40.....................	98	91	96	85
30.....................	93	86	91	79
20.....................	87	76	85	71
10.....................	79	65	77	54
0.....................	51	28	54	33

Ex. 46. Bring in illustrative material from educational periodicals showing the use of graphic methods. Bring in material showing the use of percentiles.

CHAPTER V

FREQUENCY CURVES AND THE NORMAL PROBABILITY CURVE

The Frequency Curve. In Chapter I we saw how to represent a *frequency distribution* graphically by means of a *histogram* or *frequency polygon*. Now if the total frequency in a distribution is large, and the class-interval is small, the frequency polygon or histogram will approximate rather closely to a smooth curve. As the frequency becomes larger, and the class-interval smaller, the frequency polygon and histogram will approach more and more closely to a smooth curve. In statistics, certain "smoothing" processes are often applied to histogram and frequency polygon to bring out the resemblance to a smooth curve.

Karl Pearson and others have given more exact mathematical means to determine the equation of the *frequency curve* for a given distribution, that is, the *smooth curve which is the best "fit" for the data of a particular distribution.*

The Normal Distribution. The graphs which were made in answer to Exs. 9 and 10 of Chapter I, as well as many others which might be drawn from educational, biological, anthropometrical, or economic data, have the same general form—the measures are concentrated closely around the center, and taper off from this central high point in fairly symmetric fashion. There are very few low and equally few high measures. These distributions approximate *symmetric frequency curves.*

Now mathematics offers an explanation of just why all these graphs assume this particular form. Fig. 22 illustrates the form of the perfectly *symmetric* mathematical curve to which these graphs approximate. This bell-shaped curve is called a *normal frequency curve*; it is of great importance in the field of educational measurement.

It must not be thought, however, that the normal distribution is the only type which is likely to occur in educational measurement, or in measurement in any of the sciences. Students in the field of educational statistics seem prone to expect the normal type of distribution too frequently. Thorndike says, "There is nothing arbitrary or mysterious about variability which makes the so-called normal type of distribution a necessity, or any more rational than any other sort, or even more to be expected on a priori grounds. Nature does not abhor irregular distributions."[1]

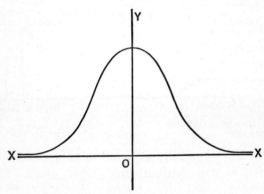

FIG. 22.—The normal curve

Pearson has developed a variety of different curves to describe these non-normal distributions. *The resemblance of a frequency distribution to a normal curve cannot be determined by a mere inspection of the data or a graph of the results. A rigorous test and a determination of the proper Pearson curve require considerable mathematical study.* Although we shall not make a study of these curves, we shall describe several types of *non-normal distributions.*

Skewed Distributions. Some of the Pearson frequency curves are devised to fit "skewed" distributions. A *skewed* distribution may be roughly described as one which is *moderately asymmetric.* (See Figs. 23 and 24.) The frequencies decrease more rapidly on one side of the modal value than on the other. *The skewed dis-*

[1] "Mental and Social Measurements," pp. 88-9.

tribution is probably the most common type of distribution occurring in educational statistics (or, in fact, in all statistics). In the normal distribution, mean, median, and mode coincide. In the skewed distribution, they fall at different points. Pearson has given as a formula for *skewness*:

$$\text{Skewness} = \frac{\text{mean} - \text{mode}}{\sigma}$$

The *true* mode is often hard to determine, and hence for convenience the formula may be altered by making use of the follow-

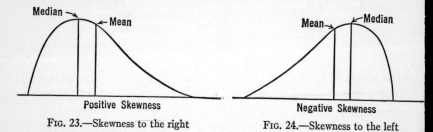

Fig. 23.—Skewness to the right   Fig. 24.—Skewness to the left

ing relation which Pearson has found to be approximately true in moderately skewed distributions.

$$\text{Mean} - \text{mode} = 3 \ (\text{mean} - \text{median})$$

Substituting this, the above formula becomes

$$\text{Skewness} = \frac{3 \ (\text{mean} - \text{median})}{\sigma}$$

Fig. 23 illustrates *positive* skewness or skewness to the *right*. Fig. 24 illustrates *negative* skewness or skewness to the *left*.

An examination of the formula indicates that, the farther apart the mean and the median are, the greater the skewness; and the closer together they are, the smaller the skewness.

For a normal distribution:

$$\text{Mean} = \text{mode, and skewness} = \frac{3(0)}{\sigma} = 0$$

Ex. 1. Find the skewness of the distributions of Tables 8, 11, and 14.

J- and U-Shaped Distributions. Figs. 25 and 26 illustrate *J-shaped distributions*. In such distributions the frequency constantly increases or decreases. Thus we have two possibilities— many low scores, fewer moderate-sized scores, and very few

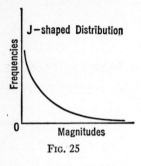

FIG. 25

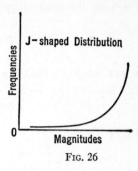

FIG. 26

high scores (Fig. 25), or very few low scores, more moderate-sized scores, and many high scores (Fig. 26). Such distributions are not very common in educational statistics, but are more likely to occur in other fields. A J-shaped distribution of the type illustrated in Fig. 25 arises in *economics* in dealing with questions of supply or demand, or the distribution of wealth. Table 11 in this text illustrates a J-shaped distribution from an educational source.

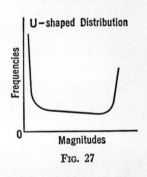

FIG. 27

Fig. 27 illustrates the *U-shaped distribution*, in which there are many low scores, many high scores, and few moderate-sized scores. Like the J-shaped distribution, this type of distribution does not arise very frequently from educational data.

Ex. 2. Illustrate, with hypothetical educational data, what you would consider a J-shaped frequency distribution; a U-shaped distribution.

Probability. Although the normal distribution is not the most frequently occurring type in educational measurement, an understanding of its properties is an essential background for a most important topic in educational measurement, namely, *the reli-*

ability of measures. In order to provide such a background, we shall enter upon some elementary mathematical considerations in the *theory of probability.*

If an event may happen in h ways and fail in f ways, mathematics defines the *probability* p that it will happen as

$$p = \frac{h}{h+f}$$

and the probability q that it will fail to happen as

$$q = \frac{f}{h+f}$$

Note that:

$$p + q = \frac{h}{h+f} + \frac{f}{h+f} = \frac{h+f}{h+f} = 1$$

that is, the sum of the probabilities of occurrence and nonoccurrence is 1.

Ex. 3. If a coin is tossed, what is the probability that it will fall head up? There are two possibilities in this case. The coin may fall head up or tail up.

$$h = 1$$
$$f = 1$$
$$p = \frac{h}{h+f} = \frac{1}{2}$$

Ex. 4. A die is tossed. What is the probability of obtaining an ace?

$$h = 1$$
$$h + f = 6$$
$$p = \frac{1}{6}$$

Ex. 5. A ball is drawn at random from a bag containing 3 red balls and 5 white balls. What is the probability of drawing a red ball?

$$p = \frac{3}{3+5} = \frac{3}{8}$$

Ex. 6. A bag contains 3 red, 4 black, and 2 white balls. If one ball is drawn at random, what is the probability that it is a black ball? a black or a white ball?

Ex. 7. From a pack of 52 cards one card is drawn. What is the probability that it will be a queen? a king or a queen?

Ex. 8. If a die is thrown, what is the probability that 5 will turn up? that 3 or 5 will turn up?

Ex. 9. If the probability of winning a game is $\frac{1}{3}$, what is the probability of losing?

Ex. 10. If the probability of the occurrence of an event is 5 times the probability of its non-occurrence, what is the probability of its occurrence?

Ex. 11. If the probability of winning is $\frac{3}{5}$, how many times would you expect to win in playing 100 games?

Coin-Tossing. The probabilities which occur in questions of coin-tossing are closely related to statistical theory, and hence a brief study of such probabilities will be made.

In Ex. 1 above, we have seen that if one coin is tossed it must fall either heads or tails. The situation may be described symbolically by H or T.

The probability of obtaining heads is $\frac{1}{2}$, and the probability of obtaining tails is $\frac{1}{2}$. Symbolically:

$$H + T = \tfrac{1}{2} + \tfrac{1}{2} = 1$$

and a table of probabilities may be written

Number of heads	Probability
1	$\frac{1}{2}$
0	$\frac{1}{2}$
Total	1

Suppose 100 trials were made with a single coin. The table of expected or *theoretical* frequencies would be

Number of heads	Expected frequency
1	50
0	50
Total	100

Now if two coins are tossed, the possibilities are as follows:

$$HH \qquad HT \qquad TH \qquad TT$$

that is, both coins may fall heads, the first may fall heads and the second tails, the first may fall tails and the second heads, or both coins may fall tails.

The probabilities are as follows:

2 heads $\frac{1}{4}$ (There are 4 possibilities in all, and one of these is the possibility of throwing 2 heads.)

1 head $\frac{1}{2}$ (There are 4 possibilities in all, and 2 of these will yield
(and 1 tail)   1 head and 1 tail, namely, the second and third possibilities above.)

0 heads $\frac{1}{4}$ (There are 4 possibilities in all and 1 of these is the possi-
(and 2 tails)   bility of 0 heads.)

A table of probabilities would be

Number of heads	Probability
2....................	$\frac{1}{4}$
1....................	$\frac{1}{2}$
0....................	$\frac{1}{4}$
Total.............	1

If 100 trials were made with 2 coins the expected or theoretical frequencies would be:

Number of heads	Expected frequency
2....................	25
1....................	50
0....................	25
Total.............	100

The above probabilities might be grouped symbolically as follows:

$$H^2 + 2HT + T^2 =$$
$$\frac{1}{4} + 2 \cdot \frac{1}{4} + \frac{1}{4} = 1$$

Note that the form of this expression is

$$(H + T)^2$$

Suppose that three coins are tossed. The possibilities are

$$HHH \quad HHT \quad HTH \quad HTT \quad THH \quad THT \quad TTH \quad TTT$$

In this case, the table of probabilities would be:

Number of heads	Probability
3....................	$\frac{1}{8}$
2....................	$\frac{3}{8}$
1....................	$\frac{3}{8}$
0....................	$\frac{1}{8}$
Total.............	1

If 96 trials were made with 3 coins, the table of theoretical frequencies would be:

Number of heads	Expected frequency
3....................	12
2....................	36
1....................	36
0....................	12
Total.............	96

Let us remark here that, in making a table of expected frequencies, we have always chosen a fairly large number of trials, inasmuch as the *theoretical frequency, as determined by mathematics, and the actual frequency, as determined by experience, correspond more closely, the larger the number of trials*.

For the case of 3 coins, we have, symbolically:

$$H^3 + 3H^2T + 3HT^2 + T^3 =$$
$$\frac{1}{8} + 3 \cdot \frac{1}{8} + 3 \cdot \frac{1}{8} + \frac{1}{8} = 1$$

Note that the form of this expression is

$$(H + T)^3$$

These results can be generalized, and it is known that, *if n coins are tossed, the probabilities of obtaining n, n − 1, n − 2, . . . 1, 0, heads are given symbolically by terms of* $(H + T)^n$.

The Binomial Theorem. The binomial theorem can be applied in carrying out expansions of this sort. This theorem states that

$$(a + b)^n = a^n + na^{n-1}b + \frac{n(n-1)}{1 \cdot 2}a^{n-2}b^2$$
$$+ \frac{n(n-1)(n-2)}{1 \cdot 2 \cdot 3 \cdot}a^{n-3}b^3 + \ldots + b^n$$

We observe the following facts:

1. The powers of a decrease from n to 0.

2. The powers of b increase from 0 to n.

3. The coefficient of the first term is 1 and of the second term n.

4. If the coefficient of each term is multiplied by the exponent of a in that term and divided by one more than the exponent of b, the coefficient of the next term is obtained.

Ex. 12. Expand the following by the binomial theorem: (a) $(x + y)^5$. (b) $(x + y)^7$. (c) $(a - b)^9$. (d) $(a - b)^{12}$. (e) $(a + 2b)^4$. (f) $(2a - b)^5$. (g) $(2a + 3b)^3$.

Probability Polygon and Histogram. For the case of 8 coins we have:

$$(H + T)^8 = H^8 + 8H^7T + 28H^6T^2 + 56H^5T^3$$
$$+ 70H^4T^4 + 56H^3T^5 + 28H^2T^6 + 8HT^7 + T^8$$

Putting $H = \frac{1}{2}$, $T = \frac{1}{2}$ into this expression, we obtain the probabilities, and we have the *probability table* for 8 coins.

TABLE 42

Number of heads	Probability
8	$\frac{1}{256}$
7	$\frac{8}{256}$
6	$\frac{28}{256}$
5	$\frac{56}{256}$
4	$\frac{70}{256}$
3	$\frac{56}{256}$
2	$\frac{28}{256}$
1	$\frac{8}{256}$
0	$\frac{1}{256}$
Total	1

Fig. 28 shows the *probability polygon* and the *histogram* of this probability table. Note that the area of the first rectangle in the histogram is $\frac{1}{256}$, of the second $\frac{8}{256}$, etc. The area of each rec-

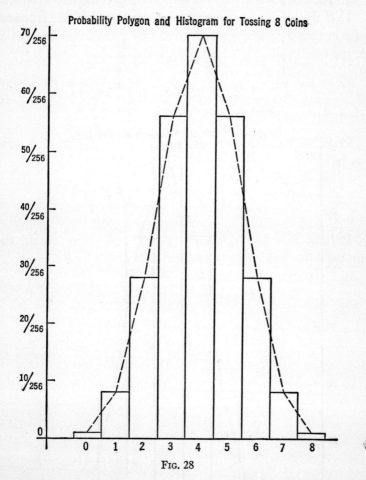

Probability Polygon and Histogram for Tossing 8 Coins

FIG. 28

tangle is equal to a probability. *The area under the whole histogram will therefore equal the sum of the probabilities, and hence this area is* 1.

In 256 trials with 8 coins the table of theoretical frequencies would be

TABLE 43

Number of heads	Expected frequency
8	1
7	8
6	28
5	56
4	70
3	56
2	28
1	8
0	1
Total	256

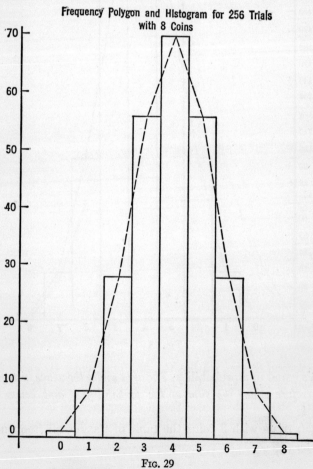

Frequency Polygon and Histogram for 256 Trials with 8 Coins

Fig. 29

Fig. 29 shows the frequency polygon and the histogram of this table. Note that this picture is exactly the same as Fig. 28, except that the readings along the Y axis are 256 times as great. Note that the area of the first rectangle in the histogram is 1,

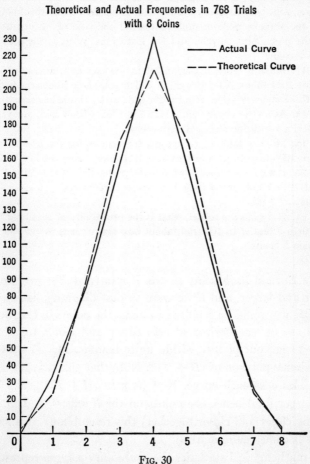

FIG. 30

of the second 8, etc., so that the *total area under the entire histogram will be equal to the total frequency*, in this case, 256.

Ex. 13. Make a table of the theoretical frequencies in 768 trials with 8 coins. In Fig. 30 this theoretical frequency table has been plotted, and along with it, the actual frequency table resulting from 768 actual trials with 8 coins made by a group of the author's students.

Ex. 14. Make a table of probabilities for the case of tossing 7 coins. Plot the probability polygon and the histogram. What is the area under this histogram?

Ex. 15. Make a table of theoretical frequencies for the case of tossing 7 coins 512 times. Alter the graph which you made in answer to the last question to fit this frequency table. What is the area under this histogram?

Ex. 16. Make a table of probabilities for the case of tossing 10 coins. Plot the probability polygon and the histogram. What is the area under the histogram?

Ex. 17. Make a table of theoretical frequencies for the case of tossing 10 coins 1024 times. Alter the graph which you made in answer to Ex. 16 to fit this frequency table. What is the area under this histogram?

Ex. 18. As a class experiment, make 256 trials with 6 coins and compare the obtained with the expected frequencies.

Ex. 19. Make a table of theoretical frequencies for the case of tossing 12 coins 4096 times. Plot a histogram and frequency polygon for these data.

Ex. 20. If 4 coins are tossed, what is the probability of obtaining 4 heads? 3 heads and 1 tail? In 64 trials how many times would you expect to get 2 heads and 2 tails?

Ex. 21. If 5 coins are tossed, what is the probability of obtaining 5 tails? more than 3 heads? In 100 trials about how many times would you expect to obtain 5 heads?

The Normal Probability Curve. If n in $(H + T)^n$ were to grow larger and larger, and if we were to plot diagrams like those in Fig. 28, we would be required to make the points $0, 1, 2, 3, \ldots$, $n - 1$, n, on the horizontal axis closer and closer together, in order to get our picture within finite bounds. Fig. 31 shows the probability polygon of $(H + T)^{20}$. Note that this polygon closely resembles a smooth curve. Now as n in $(H + T)^n$ grows larger and larger (and hence the points on the X axis, $0, 1, 2, 3, \ldots$, n come closer and closer together) this resemblance to a smooth curve becomes more marked.

In mathematical statistics the *probability polygon* representing $(H + T)^n$ as n grows larger and larger is said to approach a certain curve as a *limit*. This curve is the *normal probability curve*. Fig. 22 illustrates the form of this curve.

The curve approached by a *frequency polygon* of $(H + T)^n$ as n grows larger and larger is said to approach a *normal frequency curve* as a limit. Inasmuch as the probability polygon and frequency polygon of $(H + T)^n$ are identical in appearance and differ merely in readings along the Y axis, the same will be true of their limits, the normal probability and normal frequency curves, respectively. Hence Fig. 22 illustrates the form of both normal probability and normal frequency curves. If the total

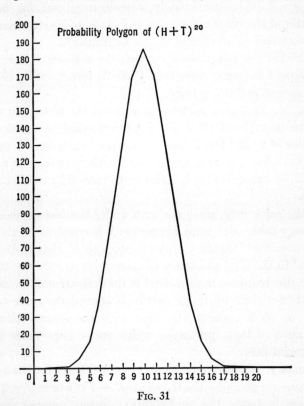

FIG. 31

frequency is N, the readings along the Y axis for the frequency polygon will be N times as great as for the probability polygon, and the same will be true of the limiting curves.

By mathematical means the equation of the *normal probability curve* can be obtained as:

$$y = \frac{1}{\sigma\sqrt{2\pi}}e^{\frac{-x^2}{2\sigma^2}}$$

and the equation of the *normal frequency curve* with total frequency N is:

$$y = \frac{N}{\sigma\sqrt{2\pi}}e^{\frac{-x^2}{2\sigma^2}}$$

where $e = 2.7183$ approximately, π has its usual meaning, namely the ratio of the circumference of any circle to its diameter, and σ = the standard deviation of the distribution.

Note that the equations show that the *ordinate of every point on a normal frequency curve is* N *times the corresponding ordinate of the normal probability curve.*

Now, we have seen that the area under the histogram of the probability table of $(H + T)^n$ is always equal to 1, whatever the value of n (and hence, however large n is). Hence it is natural to expect that the area under the limiting curve, the normal probability curve, is also 1. This can be proved by mathematical means.

In the same way, since the area under the histogram of the frequency table with total frequency N is equal to N, the area under a normal frequency curve is equal to N, that is, the area is equal to the total frequency of cases.

Since the mathematics involved in the derivation of the normal curve and a study of its properties is beyond the scope of this work, we shall content ourselves with the enumeration and application of those properties which are of importance in the educational field.

Summary. We have seen that the probabilities for the tossing of n coins are given by the terms of $(H + T)^n$ where $H = T = \frac{1}{2}$. When n is large, the probability polygon representing the probabilities resembles a smooth curve. In fact, as n grows larger and larger, this polygon approaches the *normal probability curve* as a *limit*. Thus, *the normal probability curve is the limit, as* n *becomes infinite, of the probability polygon of* $(H + T)^n$.

If a frequency polygon for N trials with n coins is plotted, its appearance will be exactly the same as the probability polygon of $(H + T)^n$. Readings along the Y axis (ordinates) however, will be N times as great. Hence, for large values of n, this frequency polygon will also resemble a smooth curve. As *n* grows larger and larger, the frequency polygon will also approach a limiting curve, whose appearance is exactly the same as that of the normal probability curve, but whose ordinates are N times as great. *A normal frequency curve for total frequency* N *is the limit, as n becomes infinite, of the frequency polygon of* $(H + T)^n$ *for total frequency* N.

The area under the normal probability curve is 1.

The area under a normal frequency curve is N.

Coin-Tossing and Educational Data. At the beginning of this chapter we asserted that many distributions obtained from educational or other sources assume an approximately normal form. Next we arrived at a mathematical definition of the normal curve by a discussion of coin-tossing. It is natural to ask how there can be any connection between coin-tossing and educational situations. Let us give an illustration to show that a similarity can exist between the situations and the results. We list the facts in parallel columns in order to bring out this analogy.

1. One hundred coins.

2. The coins should be of homogeneous construction (not loaded) so as to assure the *equal likelihood* of heads or tails. $H = T = \frac{1}{2}$.

3. *Chance factors*—the height from which a coin is thrown, the weight of the coin, the structure of the floor on which the coin falls, etc., determine whether it will fall H or T.

1. One hundred test questions.

2. We *assume* that success or failure is equally likely, that is, that a student has a "50-50" chance of getting a question right or wrong. $R = W = \frac{1}{2}$. (Corresponding to the loading of a coin, we might have excessive drill by a teacher on the type of question to be given on the test. This would make success on the part of the pupil more likely than failure. On the other hand, questions on the test might be far beyond the ability of the group of pupils being tested, and this would "load" a question the other way.)

3. *Chance factors* determine whether we have R or W. This depends on the instruction the pupil has had, his attendance at school, his interest in the subject, his innate ability to learn, his emotional state when answering the questions, etc.

4. Repeated trials.

4. Since it would hardly be possible to test the same pupil over and over, different pupils are asked the same questions.

5. At a single trial the probabilities of obtaining 100, 99, 98, . . . , 1, 0, heads are given by $(\frac{1}{2} + \frac{1}{2})^{100}$.

5. For a single pupil, the probabilities of getting 100, 99, 98, . . . , 1, 0, right are given by $(\frac{1}{2} + \frac{1}{2})^{100}$.

6. If the coins are tossed, say, 1000 times, the following tables can be filled in.

6. If the test questions are given to 1000 pupils the following tables can be filled in.

Number of heads	Expected frequency	Number right	Expected frequency
100	$(\frac{1}{2})^{100} \times 1000 = 0$ approximately	100	$(\frac{1}{2})^{100} \times 1000 = 0$ approximately
99	$100(\frac{1}{2})^{100} \times 1000$	99	$100(\frac{1}{2})^{100} \times 1000$
98	$\frac{100 \cdot 99}{1 \cdot 2}(\frac{1}{2})^{100} \times 1000$	98	$\frac{100 \cdot 99}{1 \cdot 2}(\frac{1}{2})^{100} \times 1000$
..		..	
..		..	
..		..	
0	0 approximately	0	0 approximately

Number of heads	Actual frequency	Number right	Actual frequency
100		100	
99		99	
98		98	
..		..	
..		..	
..		..	
0		0	

Note that this last table is the type of frequency table with which we are familiar.

Properties of Normal Distributions. As Fig. 22 shows, the normal probability curve and normal frequency curves are symmetric with respect to the Y axis. As we have stated above, the area between a normal frequency curve and the X axis is equal to the total frequency in the distribution, and hence, half the total area will lie on either side of the Y axis, and this axis will represent the middle of the distribution. In other words the *median* will fall at $x = 0$. Because of the symmetry of a normal distribution, the *median* and the *mean* will be the same. Note that the curve has a maximum point at $x = 0$, that is, for $x = 0$, y has its greatest value, which means that $x = 0$ is also the *mode* of the distribution.

As a result of these facts, the abscissa x of a point on the curve represents the *deviation* of a score from the mean (or median or mode).

Table 44 gives the area *under the normal probability curve and included between the* Y *axis and different ordinates.*

Since the total area under a normal frequency curve with total frequency N is just N times as great as the total area under the normal probability curve, and since the two curves are similar in form throughout, it is natural to expect that corresponding parts of the two areas will also be in the ratio N to 1. Hence, Table 44 also gives the *portion of the total area under any normal frequency curve and included between the* Y *axis and different ordinates,* that is, the *fraction of the total number of cases included between the mean and some other score.* Only the positive half of the curve, that is, only the cases whose scores are higher than the mean, are accounted for in this table, since the other half of the curve can be treated in symmetric fashion.

Just as in an arithmetic problem it might be helpful to change the unit from inches to feet by dividing by 12, or from cents to dollars by dividing by 100, it is helpful in working out and applying statistical tables to change the unit of measurement on the X axis to "sigmas" where σ is the standard deviation of the particular distribution which is being considered. Thus:

$$158 \text{ inches} = \frac{158}{12} \text{ feet} = 13.17 \text{ feet}$$

$$276 \text{ cents} = \frac{276}{100} \text{ dollars} = \$2.76$$

In a distribution in which $\sigma = 7$, $x = 9$ units $= \dfrac{9}{7}$ sigmas $= 1.29\ \sigma$.

Note that, since x represents a deviation from the mean, $\dfrac{x}{\sigma}$ represents a *standard score.* Hence the change of an abscissa to "sigma" units is equivalent to the change of a raw score to a standard score.

TABLE 44

TABLE OF AREAS FOR THE NORMAL PROBABILITY CURVE

Standard score $\dfrac{x}{\sigma}$	Area	Standard score $\dfrac{x}{\sigma}$	Area
0.0	0.000	2.1	0.482
0.1	.040	2.2	.486
0.2	.079	2.3	.489
0.3	.118	2.4	.492
0.4	.155	2.5	.494
0.5	.191	2.6	.495
0.6	.226	2.7	.496
0.7	.258	2.8	.497
0.8	.288	2.9	.4981
0.9	.316	3.0	.4987
1.0	.341	3.1	.4990
1.1	.364	3.2	.4993
1.2	.385	3.3	.4995
1.3	.403	3.4	.4997
1.4	.419	3.5	.4998
1.5	.433	3.6	.4998
1.6	.445	3.7	.4999
1.7	.455	3.8	.4999
1.8	.464	3.9	.5000
1.9	.471	4.0	.5000
2.0	.477	4.1	.5000

The first column of Table 44 gives the abscissa in sigmas or the standard score. Opposite 0.8 we read 0.288. This means that 0.288 is the area under the *normal probability curve* included between the Y axis and the ordinate $x = 0.8\ \sigma$.

Interpreted for a *normal frequency curve* with total frequency N it means that 0.288 N is the area under the normal frequency curve included between the Y axis and the ordinate $x = 0.8\ \sigma$, or that *0.288 or 28.8 per cent of the total number of cases is included between the mean and a score 0.8 σ above the mean.* See Fig. 32.

In terms of *standard scores*, this fact may be restated as: *28.8 per cent of the cases in a normal distribution have standard scores ranging between 0 and 0.8.*

Thus, if a normal distribution contains 1000 cases, the total area under the corresponding normal frequency curve will be

1000, and the area under this normal frequency curve included between the Y axis and the ordinate $x = 0.8\ \sigma$ will be 0.288×1000, or 288. Stated otherwise, there are 288 cases included between the mean and a score $0.8\ \sigma$ above the mean. If the mean is 70 and $\sigma = 8$, there will be 288 cases between 70 and $70 + 0.8(8)$ $= 76.4$.

Because of the symmetry of the curve, we know also that 0.288 or 28.8 per cent of the cases come between the mean and a score $0.8\ \sigma$ below the mean. In our concrete example, 288 cases will have scores between 63.6 and 70.

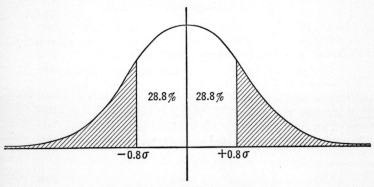

FIG. 32.—Area between Y axis and $\pm 0.8\sigma$

In terms of standard scores, then, 28.8 per cent of the cases in any normal distribution have standard scores ranging from -0.8 to 0.

Reading opposite $x = 1\sigma$, we find that the area under the normal probability curve will be 0.341, or that the area under any normal frequency curve will be $0.341N$. Stated otherwise, 0.341 or 34.1 per cent of the cases in a normal distribution fall between the mean and a score 1σ above the mean. Thus *68.2 per cent of the cases, or roughly two-thirds of the cases lie between the score 1σ below the mean and the score 1σ above the mean.* See Fig. 33.

In terms of standard scores, this may be stated as follows: *In any normal distribution, approximately two-thirds of the cases have standard scores between -1 and $+1$.*

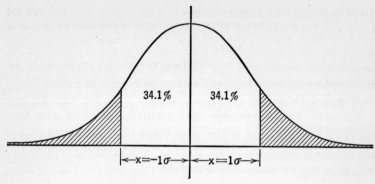

FIG. 33.—Area between −1σ and +1σ

Ex. 22. The scores of 200 pupils in a history test form a normal distribution. The mean score is 69 with a standard deviation of 9.

(a) About how many pupils obtained scores between 69 and 80?

(b) Between 60 and 69?

(c) Between 60 and 75?

(d) Between 75 and 85?

(e) What is the probability that a student will obtain a mark above 75?

(f) What chance has a student to pass if the passing grade is 65?

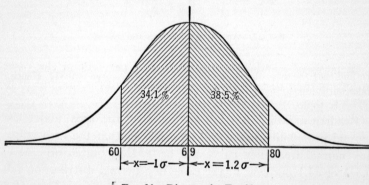

FIG. 34.—Diagram for Ex. 22

We shall work this problem so that it may serve as a model. For diagrams see Figs. 34 and 35.

(a) A mark of 80 is 11 units above the mean. Changing to σ units we have $\frac{11}{9} = 1.2 \ \sigma$, that is, in this distribution, a raw score of 80 is equivalent to a standard score of 1.2.

(Since Table 44 gives the x coordinate to tenths only, we shall find the x coordinate to tenths in our work, remembering, of course, that all results will be approximate.) Reading opposite 1.2 σ in the table, we find that 0.385 is the area under the normal probability curve. The area under our *normal frequency curve* with total area 200 is therefore 0.385 × 200 = 77. Hence approximately 77 pupils will have scores between 69 and 80.

(*b*) Now 60 is 9 units below the mean; $\frac{9}{9} = 1\sigma$, that is, the standard score corresponding to 60 is 1. Since the curve is symmetric, the number of cases between the mean and a score 1σ below the mean is the same as the number of cases between the mean and a score 1σ above the mean. We can obtain the latter information by reading opposite 1 in the table.

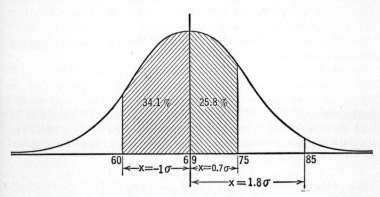

FIG. 35.—Diagram for Ex. 22

We find that the area under the normal probability curve is 0.341. Hence, under our normal frequency curve, the corresponding area will be 0.341 × 200 = 68, approximately. Hence approximately 68 pupils will have scores between 60 and 69.

(*c*) To make use of Table 44 we must reduce a problem to a question of finding the number of cases between the mean and some other score. Hence we shall answer this question by finding: (1) the number of cases between 60 and 69; (2) the number of cases between 69 and 75. (3) Then we shall add these results.

(1) is approximately 68, from (*b*). To answer (2): 75 is 6 above the mean; $\frac{6}{9} = 0.7\sigma$, approximately. From the table, 0.258 is the area for the normal probability curve. Hence, for the normal frequency curve, 0.258 × 200 = 52, approximately.

(3) 68 + 52 = 120.

(*d*) To answer this we must find: (1) the number of cases between 69 and 75; (2) the number of cases between 69 and 85, and then subtract (1) from (2). By (c), (1) is 52. To answer (2): $\frac{16}{9} = 1.8\sigma$. Using the table, 0.464×200 is approximately 93. $93 - 52 = 41$ cases between 75 and 85.

(e) Fifty per cent of the cases or 100 cases fall below the mean. From (c), 52 cases come between the mean and 75. Hence $100 + 52 = 152$ cases fall below 75, and $200 - 152 = 48$ cases fall above 75. Using the probability notation, $h = 48$, $h + f = 200$, and the probability is $\frac{48}{200} = \frac{6}{25}$.

(f) See if you can prove that the probability that a student will obtain a grade above 65 is $\frac{131}{200}$. Hence a student has a chance of 131 in 200 to pass.

Ex. 23. The scores of 500 pupils in a standardized test form a normal distribution. The mean score is 80 with a standard deviation of 12. About how many pupils obtained scores between 80 and 90? between 75 and 90? between 65 and 75? above 95? What is the probability that a student will obtain a mark below 60?

Ex. 24. In a final test in high-school geometry the students averaged 65 and the standard deviation of their marks was 10. Assuming that the marks were distributed normally, what percentage of the students received marks below 60? above 75? between 80 and 90? between 60 and 70? If 200 students took the test, approximately how many honor students were there, if a mark above 80 is considered an honor grade? What chance did a student have to obtain an honor grade?

Ex. 25. The mean I.Q. in a certain high school of 1000 pupils is 105, and σ of the distribution of I.Q.'s is 11. Assuming that this distribution is normal, what is the probability that a student's I.Q. will fall below 100? will fall between 90 and 110? Approximately how many students will have I.Q.'s higher than 110?

Ex. 26. What percentage of cases in a normal distribution will have standard scores between -0.5 and $+0.5$? between -2 and $+2$? between -3 and $+3$?

Ex. 27. In a normal distribution find the percentile rank of a student whose standard score is 1.5; whose standard score is 2.5; whose standard score is -2.

Ex. 28. In a normal distribution the mean is 60 and $\sigma = 13$. Find the percentile ranks of the following scores: 95, 85, 70, 50, 30.

Interpolation. By the use of *interpolation*, Table 44 can be used to read areas for abscissas worked out to the *hundredths* place.

Of course, we may comment here on the fact that this degree of accuracy is hardly warranted in such problems as we shall discuss in this book, or, in fact, in many educational problems. It is hardly worth while to carry figuring to a great degree of accuracy when larger inaccuracies arise from the fact that educational facts correspond only approximately to mathematical theory.

To proceed to an example, suppose it is desired to find that portion of the total area under a normal frequency curve, which is included between the mean and a point $1.14\,\sigma$ above the mean. We have:

$$
\begin{array}{c}
\dfrac{x}{\sigma} \qquad\qquad\qquad \text{Area} \\[4pt]
0.1\left[\begin{array}{l} 1.2 \\[4pt] 0.04\left[\begin{array}{l} 1.14 \\ 1.1 \end{array}\right. \end{array}\right.
\qquad
\begin{array}{r} 385 \\[4pt] \left.\begin{array}{r} ? \\ 364 \end{array}\right\}? \end{array}\left.\begin{array}{r}\\[4pt]\\[4pt]\\ \end{array}\right]21
\end{array}
$$

The change in $\dfrac{x}{\sigma}$ is $\dfrac{0.04}{0.1} = \dfrac{4}{10} = \dfrac{2}{5}$ of the total change. Assuming that the

change in area is proportional to the change in $\dfrac{x}{\sigma}$, the change in area will

also be $\dfrac{2}{5}$ of the total change. $\dfrac{2}{5} \times 21 = 8.4 = 8$, approximately.

Adding this to 364, we obtain 372. Therefore 0.372 of the total area lies between the mean and a point 1.14σ above the mean.

Let us rework part of Ex. 22, using interpolation. (a) A mark of 80 is $\dfrac{11}{9}\sigma$ above the mean, or, carrying the division of 11 by 9 to 2 decimal places, 1.22σ above the mean. We have:

$$
\begin{array}{c}
\dfrac{x}{\sigma} \qquad\qquad\qquad \text{Area} \\[4pt]
0.1\left[\begin{array}{l} 1.3 \\[4pt] 0.02\left[\begin{array}{l} 1.22 \\ 1.2 \end{array}\right. \end{array}\right.
\qquad
\begin{array}{r} 403 \\[4pt] \left.\begin{array}{r} ? \\ 385 \end{array}\right\}? \end{array}\left.\begin{array}{r}\\[4pt]\\[4pt]\\ \end{array}\right]18
\end{array}
$$

The change in $\dfrac{x}{\sigma}$ is:

$$\frac{0.02}{0.1} = \frac{2}{10} = \frac{1}{5} \text{ of the total change}$$

Hence the change in area is

$$\frac{1}{5} \times 18 = 3.6 = 4, \text{ approximately}$$

Adding this to 385 gives 389. Therefore 0.389 or 38.9 per cent of the cases will come within the given limits.

$$38.9\% \text{ of } 200 = 77.8 = 78 \text{ pupils, approximately}$$

(c) (2) The number of cases between 69 and 75.

$$\frac{6}{9}\sigma = 0.67\sigma$$

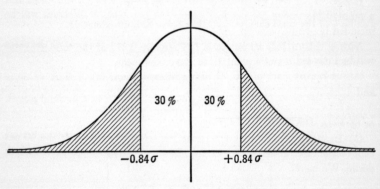

$$\frac{0.07}{0.1} = \frac{7}{10}$$

$$\frac{7}{10} \times 32 = 22.4 = 22, \text{ approximately}$$

$$226 + 22 = 248$$

Therefore 0.248 or 24.8 per cent of the cases will be included.

$$24.8\% \text{ of } 200 = 49.6 = 50 \text{ cases}$$
$$68 + 50 = 118 \text{ cases between 60 and 75}$$

FIG. 36.—Diagram for Ex. 31

Ex. 29. Complete Ex. 22 finding x in σ units to two decimal places and interpolating.

Ex. 30. Rework Exs. 23, 24, and 25, working out x in σ units to two decimal places and interpolating.

Ex. 31. If the mean of a normal distribution is 102 and $\sigma = 10$, find approximately: (a) the two limits which include the middle 60 per cent of the cases; (b) the ninth decile; (c) between what two limits practically all the cases will lie (that is, the range).

(a) The middle 60 per cent of the cases will include 30 per cent of the cases above the mean and 30 per cent below the mean. See Fig. 36.

If we examine Table 44 under the column headed Area, we do not find 0.300, but we do find two values, 0.288 and 0.316, respectively, between which 0.300 lies. We have

$$
\frac{x}{\sigma}
$$

$$
0.1 \begin{bmatrix} 0.9 & & \\ & ? \begin{bmatrix} ? \\ 0.8 \end{bmatrix} \end{bmatrix} \qquad \text{Area} \begin{bmatrix} 316 & \\ & 300 \\ & 288 \end{bmatrix} 12 \end{bmatrix} 28
$$

The change in area is

$$
\frac{12}{28} = \frac{3}{7} \text{ of the total change}
$$

Hence the change in $\frac{x}{\sigma}$ is

$$
\frac{3}{7} \times 0.1 = 0.04, \text{ approximately}
$$

$$
0.8 + 0.04 = 0.84
$$

Hence 30 per cent of the cases will be included between the mean and a point 0.84σ above the mean. Likewise 30 per cent of the cases will be included between the mean and a point 0.84σ below the mean.

Now $\sigma = 10$. Hence $0.84\sigma = 8.4$, and the middle 60 per cent of the cases will be included between

$$
102 - 8.4
$$

and

$$
102 + 8.4
$$

or between 93.6 and 110.4.

(b) By using Table 44 we determine the score which bounds the 40 per cent of the cases above the mean, for this score will obviously be the ninth decile. We have:

$$
\frac{x}{\sigma}
$$

$$
0.1 \begin{bmatrix} 1.3 & & \\ & ? \begin{bmatrix} ? \\ 1.2 \end{bmatrix} \end{bmatrix} \qquad \text{Area} \begin{bmatrix} 403 & \\ & 400 \\ & 385 \end{bmatrix} 15 \end{bmatrix} 18 \end{bmatrix}
$$

$$
\frac{15}{18} = \frac{5}{6}
$$

$$
\frac{5}{6} \times 0.1 = 0.08, \text{ approximately}
$$

$$
1.2 + 0.08 = 1.28
$$

Hence 40 per cent of the cases will be included between the mean and a point 1.28σ above the mean, or between 102 and $102 + (1.28)(10) = 114.8$.

(c) Now, from the table we see that opposite 3.9σ the reading is 0.5000 (when rounded off to 4 decimal places) and hence practically all the cases will lie between $102 - 3.9\sigma$ and $102 + 3.9\sigma$ or between 63 and 141.

NOTE: *For practical purposes, the normal curve is often treated as ending at 3σ below the mean and 3σ above the mean, since we see from the table that 99.7 per cent of the cases will lie between these limits.*

In much of the work that follows we shall also make this assumption.

Ex. 32. The mean mark in English of a group of high-school seniors was 75 with a standard deviation of 5. If the marks were distributed normally, approximately what limits include the middle two-thirds of the cases? What limits include the middle 85 per cent of the cases? the middle 75 per cent of the cases? Using the note in Ex. 31, find the approximate range for all cases.

Ex. 33. In a normal distribution, the mean is 100 and $\sigma = 14$. Find the scores whose percentile ranks are 30, 60, 75, 90.

Ex. 34. In a normal distribution, the mean is 60 and $\sigma = 8$. Find the scores whose percentile ranks are 15, 40, 65, 80. Find the approximate range for all cases.

The Probable Error. If we use Table 44 to find limits for the middle 50 per cent of the cases in a normal distribution, that is, to find Q_1 and Q_3, we have:

$$\frac{x}{\sigma} \qquad\qquad \text{Area}$$

$$0.1\begin{bmatrix} 0.7 & 0.258 \\ ?\begin{bmatrix} ? \\ 0.6 \end{bmatrix} & \begin{bmatrix} 0.250 \\ 0.226 \end{bmatrix}24 \end{bmatrix}32$$

$$\frac{24}{32} = \frac{3}{4}$$

$$\frac{3}{4} \times 0.1 = 0.07$$

$$x = 0.67\sigma$$

Thus the approximate values of Q_1 and Q_3, in a normal distribution are:

$$\text{Mean} - 0.67\ \sigma$$

and

$$\text{Mean} + 0.67\ \sigma$$

By the use of much more accurate tables, the approximate value 0.67 σ becomes 0.6744898 σ.

In other words, *in a normal distribution*, the semi-interquartile range $Q = 0.6744898\ \sigma$.

This value is known in statistics as the *probable error*; that is, in a normal distribution, the *probable error* is just another name for the semi-interquartile range, and

$$\text{P.E.} = 0.6744898\ \sigma$$

$$\text{Roughly, P.E.} = \frac{2}{3}\ \sigma.$$

For an explanation of the nomenclature, we must wait for the material of the next chapter, where the connection of the Q of a normal distribution with errors will become clearer.

The P.E. is frequently used as a unit of measurement in just the way we have used σ, that is, the abscissas are expressed in P.E.'s instead of in sigmas, and use is made of a table like Table 44, but with a heading "abscissa in P.E.'s." This is chiefly a matter of tradition, since the early work in statistics made use of the P.E. in this way.

In the following exercises, use the approximation $\text{P.E.} = \frac{2}{3}\ \sigma$:

Ex. 35. In a normal distribution $\sigma = 3.5$. What does P.E. equal?

Ex. 36. In a normal distribution $Q = 7$. What does σ equal?

Ex. 37. In a normal distribution 3 P.E. equals how many sigmas? $2\sigma =$ how many P.E.'s?

Ex. 38. In a normal distribution, what are the chances that a score will fall between the limits: mean $-$ P.E., and mean $+$ P.E.? What are the chances that a score will fall outside these limits?

Ex. 39. In a normal distribution of 1000 cases the mean $= 70$ and the P.E. $= 5$. What percentage of the cases will fall between 75 and 80? between 75 and 85? between 85 and 90?

Ex. 40. In a certain college, the students spent, on the average, $31.50 each year for their books. If $Q = \$3.10$, for the distribution of their expenditures, and if this distribution is normal, what limits include the expenditures of the 25 per cent who spent least? the 10 per cent who spent most?

Ex. 41. In a normal distribution, the mean $= 75$ and the P.E. $= 6$. Find Q_1, Q_3, the first decile, the 65th percentile. Find the scores whose percentile ranks are 20, 40, 70, 95.

Ex. 42. One hundred high-school seniors are to receive grades on a certain test. The grades to be given are A, B, C, D, and E, and the range of ability is to be the same for each grade. Assuming that the students form a *normal* or nearly normal group with respect to the capacity which the test measures, how many students should receive each of the grades A, B, C, D, E?

Let us represent the positions of the five groups A, B, C, D, E on a diagram of the normal curve. See Fig. 37. Assume, as in the note above, that the curve ends at mean $- 3\sigma$ and mean $+ 3\sigma$. Hence the length of the base line is 6σ. Dividing this by 5, we get 1.2σ as the difference between limits for each group. From the figure it is evident that the C group has

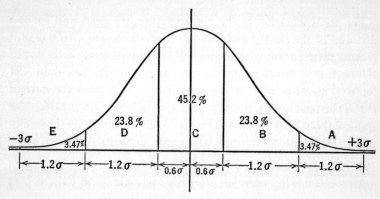

Fig. 37.—Normal distribution of grades

as its limits mean $- 0.6\sigma$ and mean $+ 0.6\sigma$; that the B group has as its limits mean $+ 0.6\sigma$ and mean $+ 1.8\sigma$; and the A group mean $+ 1.8\sigma$ and mean $+ 3\sigma$. The D and E groups occupy positions symmetric to the B and A groups respectively.

From Table 44 we see that between the mean and 3σ there are 49.87 per cent of the cases. Between the mean and 1.8σ there are 46.4 per cent of the cases.

$$49.87 - 46.4 = 3.47\% \text{ of the cases in the A group}$$
$$3.47\% \text{ of } 100 = 3.5, \text{ approximately}$$

Hence there are 3 or 4 students in the A group. By symmetry there are also 3 or 4 students in the E group.

Between the mean and 0.6σ lie 22.6 per cent of the cases.

$$46.4 - 22.6 = 23.8\% \text{ of the cases in the B group}$$
$$23.8\% \text{ of } 100 = 24 \text{ students, approximately}$$

There are also 24 students in the D group.

To get the number in the C group:

$$22.6 + 22.6 = 45.2\% \text{ in the C group}$$
$$45.2\% \text{ of } 100 = 45 \text{ students, approximately, in the C group}$$

Thus we have:

A	B	C	D	E
4	24	45	24	3

or else 3 students might have been placed in the A group and 4 in the E group.

Ex. 43. Apportion grades, A, B, C, D, normally among 100 students.

Ex. 44. Apportion grades A, B, C, D, E, F, G, normally among 150 students.

Summary. In this chapter we have discussed some of the types of frequency distribution arising from educational data. In connection with the normal type we have discussed the *normal probability curve*, studied some of its elementary properties, and applied these to educational data.

REVIEW QUESTIONS

Ex. 45. In a normal distribution the mean is 105 and the standard deviation 11. What percentage of the cases will fall between 110 and 120? Find the percentile rank of 100. Find the approximate range in scores.

Ex. 46. In a normal distribution, the mean is 157 and $Q = 15$. What limits include the middle 75 per cent of the cases? Find Q_1 and Q_3. Find approximate limits for the lowest 10 per cent of the cases.

Ex. 47. Mark the following true or false:

(1) In a normal distribution 5 P.E. $= 3\frac{1}{3}\sigma$ approximately.

(2) The normal distribution is the most frequently occurring type in educational measurement.

(3) In a normal distribution: Mean $-$ mode $= 3$(mean $-$ median).

(4) If two skewed distributions have equal means and equal medians, the more variable of the two distributions has the greater skewness.

(5) The probability that a score will be lower than Mean $-$ 5 P.E. is practically zero.

(6) The skewness of a normal distribution is equal to zero.

(7) If the mean is greater than the median, a distribution has negative skewness.

(8) If 2 distributions have equal means and equal medians, respectively, they have equal skewness.

(9) Practically all cases in a normal distribution will be included between the limits: Mean $\pm$ 4.5 P.E.

(10) If the median is greater than the mean, a distribution is skewed to the left.

(11) The probability that a score will be included between the limits Mean $\pm$ σ is approximately $\frac{2}{3}$.

Ex. 48. Bring in material from educational periodicals to illustrate the use of the normal curve.

CHAPTER VI

RELIABILITY OF MEASURES

Errors Due to Sampling. In making educational measurements, as in making measurements of any sort, there are naturally many sources of error. Just as, in determining weights with an imperfect balance, all weights may be too large or too small, so may all scores on a test be too high or too low according as the test questions are too easy or too hard. Also, if scores are based on the judgment of examiners, they may all be too high or too low according to the severity or leniency of the examiners. If such errors are recognized, compensation can be made, just as a simple addition or subtraction may correct an error in weighing.

There exists another type of error which can be studied by statistical methods. To illustrate concretely, let us suppose that the mean achievement of all 12-year-old children in the United States in a certain standardized arithmetic test is desired. Now it is hardly possible to administer such a test to *all* 12-year-olds, or even a fair percentage of them. The best we can do is to give the test to as large and representative a group of these as possible—that is, to give it to some 12-year-olds in every state, in every type of community—urban or rural, wealthy or poor, native or foreign, etc. Such a group is called a *sample*.

What we actually can obtain is the mean achievement of this sample, and use it as the best obtainable *approximation* to the *true mean* of all 12-year-olds. How reliable an approximation it will be can be ascertained by statistical means. Statistical methods can determine the *sampling error* in the mean, namely, the difference between the true mean and the mean obtained from the sample.

We shall give the formulas involved, and explain their applica-

111

tion, without having recourse to the derivations of these formulas, which involve mathematics too difficult for the layman.

Standard Error of the Mean. Suppose, for example, the mean score of 100,000 children in a certain test is desired and that the score obtained from a sample of 1000 is 81. If a different sample of 1000 had been taken, a different mean score would probably have been obtained. As it is evident that 100 different samples of 1000 might have been taken, a frequency table like the following might have resulted.

The mean of the means of all the samples, or the true mean,[1] is 79.12, and the standard deviation, or σ of the distribution of means in Table 45 is 1.65. The mean obtained, 81, differs from the true mean by 1.88, and hence the sampling error, in this case, is 1.88.

TABLE 45

Value of the mean	Number of samples giving this value
83	2
82	6
81	13
80	19
79	23
78	21
77	11
76	4
75	1
	$N = 100$

Now, in practice, only one sample would be available, namely, the one we have used, and it would be necessary for us to de-

[1] Note that the mean of the means of all the samples is the same as the true mean (that is, the mean score of the 100,000 children), since the mean of the means of all the samples is

$$\frac{83 \times 2 + 82 \times 6 + \ldots + 76 \times 4 + 75 \times 1}{100}$$

and the true mean is

$$\frac{83 \times 2000 + 82 \times 6000 + \ldots + 75 \times 1000}{100,000}$$

Dividing numerator and denominator of the last fraction by 1000 yields the same result as for the mean of the means of the samples.

termine the reliability of the mean obtained, and without knowledge of the means of other samples. A table like Table 45 would not be available. It can be shown mathematically, however, that the *standard error of the mean* is given by the formula

$$\sigma_M = \frac{\sigma_s}{\sqrt{N}}$$

where σ_s = the standard deviation of the sample and N = the total frequency of the sample.

The standard error of the mean is the standard deviation of the distribution of means which would be obtained by taking all possible samples, that is, the standard deviation of a distribution analogous to that in Table 45.

The larger σ_M, the more varied this distribution would be, and the less reliable the mean obtained from any particular sample would be. σ_M might be called the *unreliability* of the mean.

The formula for σ_M seems reasonable, since the larger the denominator of the fraction, the smaller the value of the fraction (that is, the smaller the unreliability, and the greater the reliability). This is what we would expect. A larger value of N means a larger sample, and we would naturally expect a more reliable mean. Also a larger numerator increases the size of σ_M. Again, this seems natural. If our sample shows great variability, we would not expect the mean obtained from it to be very reliable.

Now, it is assumed that *if the size of the sample is large, and if the total population being sampled is very large, the distribution of means analogous to that in Table 45 will be approximately normal.* This fact enables us to find approximate limits for the true mean, using σ_M and the mean obtained from the sample.

Ex. 1. Table 46 gives the scores of a sample of college students on a "militarism-pacifism" scale. High scores represent tendencies toward pacifism; low scores represent militaristic inclinations.

TABLE 46*

SCORES OF VARIOUS GROUPS IN MILITARISM-PACIFISM SCALE

Class	Number of cases	Mean score in militarism-pacifism scale	σ
Freshmen..............	8	11.23	2.02
Sophomores...........	136	11.32	2.35
Juniors...............	96	11.56	2.05
Seniors...............	66	11.93	2.30
Graduates.............	83	12.38	2.16

* Data from "A Scale of Militarism-Pacifism," by D. D. Droba, *Journal of Educational Psychology*, February, 1931.

Between what two limits does the true mean militarism-pacifism score of all college sophomores probably lie?

$$\sigma_M = \frac{\sigma_s}{\sqrt{N}} = \frac{2.35}{\sqrt{136}} = 0.20$$

We assume that all the means which could be obtained from different samples of college sophomores would form a normal distribution, having as its mean the *true mean militarism-pacifism score for sophomores*.

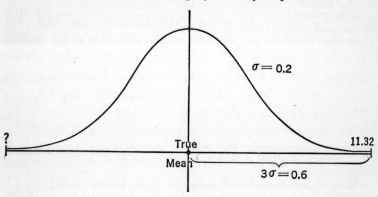

FIG. 38.—Diagram for Ex. 1

$\sigma_M = 0.20$ is the standard deviation of this normal distribution.

Now if, by chance, this sample of sophomores has obtained the highest mean which any sample will yield, 11.32 will occupy the position of the upper limit of scores in this normal distribution. See Fig. 38. Since, in a normal distribution, the highest score is approximately 3σ above the mean, we have

$$\text{True mean} + 0.6 = 11.32$$
$$\therefore \text{True mean} = 11.32 - 0.6 = 10.72$$

If, by chance, this sample of sophomores has obtained the lowest mean which any sample will yield, 11.32 will occupy the position of the lower limit of scores in this normal distribution. See Fig. 39. In this case we have

$$\text{True mean} - 0.6 = 11.32$$
$$\text{True mean} = 11.92$$

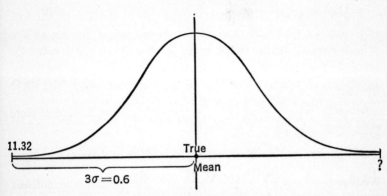

FIG. 39.—Diagram for Ex. 1

Thus, in these *extreme* cases, the true mean will have the values indicated. If the mean of this sample of sophomores occupies any other position in the normal distribution, it will differ from the true mean by less than 3σ,

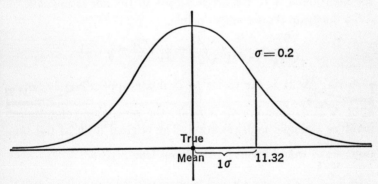

FIG. 40.—Diagram for Ex. 1

and hence the true mean will not be as low as 10.72 or as high as 11.92. For example, if, by chance, the mean of this sample of sophomores were to occupy a position 1σ above the true mean (see Fig. 40), we would have

$$\text{True mean} + 0.2 = 11.32$$
$$\text{True mean} = 11.12$$

In any case, the true mean lies somewhere between 10.72 and 11.92 approximately.

The limits for the true mean, then, can always be found by taking

$$M_s \pm 3\sigma_M$$

where M_s = the mean of the sample.

Transformation of Radicals. As an aid in the use of the formula for the standard error of the mean, and in the use of the other formulas of this chapter, the student should review briefly the following two principles often used in algebra for the transformation of square roots. To shorten numerical work, the table of square roots will be found to be of great assistance.

1. *Remove from under the radical sign any factor whose square root can be found.*

2. *Rationalize the denominator of a fraction containing a radical.*

Thus

$$\sqrt{150} = \sqrt{25 \cdot 6} = 5\sqrt{6}$$
$$\sqrt{500} = \sqrt{100 \cdot 5} = 10\sqrt{5}$$

The latter forms are often more convenient if a brief table of square roots is the only one available. If, say, a table of square roots of numbers from 1 to 100 is available, it can be applied to the final, but not to the original form of the above radicals.

To illustrate the second principle,

$$\frac{9}{\sqrt{21}} = \frac{9}{\sqrt{21}} \cdot \frac{\sqrt{21}}{\sqrt{21}} = \frac{9}{21}\sqrt{21} = \frac{3}{7}\sqrt{21}$$

Again, $\frac{3}{7}\sqrt{21}$ is far easier to evaluate approximately, since, after $\sqrt{21}$ is found from a table, the remaining computation involves a simple multiplication. The original form of the fraction, $\frac{9}{\sqrt{21}}$, would involve an arduous long division.

Ex. 2. Transform the following radicals by using the principles listed above:

(a) $\sqrt{98}$. (b) $\sqrt{112}$. (c) $\sqrt{108}$. (d) $\sqrt{294}$.

(e) $\sqrt{75}$. (f) $\frac{8}{\sqrt{10}}$. (g) $\frac{2}{\sqrt{24}}$. (h) $\frac{10}{\sqrt{50}}$.

(i) $\frac{3}{\sqrt{200}}$. (j) $\frac{7}{\sqrt{20}}$. (k) $\frac{9}{\sqrt{56}}$.

Ex. 3. In a standardized test the mean score of 10-year-old children is 50, and $\sigma = 12$. One hundred children were tested. Between what two limits does the true mean score of all 10-year-old children probably lie?

Ex. 4. Using the data of Table 46 find the probable limits for the mean militarism-pacifism score of all college seniors.

Ex. 5. Find limits for the mean militarism-pacifism score of all college freshmen; all college juniors; all college graduates. For which class of students in Table 46 is the mean most reliable? least reliable? Why?

Now, *in giving statistical results*, it is customary not to give the extreme limits for the mean, that is, not to give the entire possible range for the true mean, but to observe a convention which we shall explain.

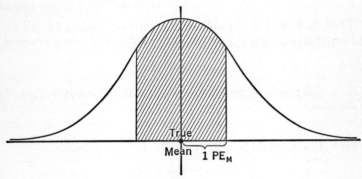

Fig. 41.—Cases between Mean ± 1P.E.$_M$

If the true mean does not differ from the mean of the sample by more than 1 P.E.$_M$ $\left(\dfrac{2}{3}\sigma_M \text{ approximately}\right)$, the mean of the sample will occupy a position somewhere in the base of the shaded area in Fig. 41.

In this case, we have:

$$\text{True mean} = M_s \pm 1 \text{ P.E.}_M$$

Since 50 per cent of the cases in a normal distribution lie between the limits Mean ± 1 P.E. the probability is $\frac{1}{2}$ that the mean of the sample lies in the base of the shaded area in Fig. 41, and hence the probability that

$$\text{True mean} = M_s \pm 1 \text{ P.E.}_M$$

is also $\frac{1}{2}$.

Hence the chances are even that the limits

$$\text{True mean} = M_s \pm 1 \text{ P.E.}_M$$

are correct.

The use of these limits gives a narrower range for the true mean, and it is customary to give the limits in this form in statistical reports and publications.

Hence, in Ex. 1, the limits in this form are

$$\text{Mean} \pm \frac{2}{3}(0.20) = \text{mean} \pm 0.13$$
$$= 11.32 \pm 0.13$$

Thus, in a statistical publication, if it were desired to indicate the reliability of this mean, it would be listed as

$$\text{Mean} = 11.32 \pm 0.13$$

Ex. 6. Using your results for Exs. 4 and 5, list all means in Table 46 in the form

$$\text{Mean} \pm \text{P.E.}_M.$$

Ex. 7. In a statistical journal, the results of a test are stated:

$$\text{Mean} = 67.5 \pm 1.2$$

Find σ_M and the entire possible range of values for the true mean.

$$\text{P.E.}_M = \frac{2}{3}\sigma_M, \text{ approximately}$$

or

$$\sigma_M = \frac{3}{2} \text{ P.E.}_M, \text{ approximately}$$
$$\text{P.E.}_M = 1.2$$

Hence $\qquad \sigma_M = \frac{3}{2}(1.2) = 1.8, \text{ approximately.}$

$$\text{Entire range} = M_s \pm 3\sigma_M = 67.5 \pm 5.4$$

Ex. 8. The mean I.Q. of a sample is 101 ± 2.3. Find σ_M. Between what two limits does the true mean of the entire group probably lie?

Ex. 9. In Table 48 find the standard error of each mean listed under the heading Freshmen. Give extreme limits for the true mean in each case. Write each mean in the form customarily used in statistical publications to indicate the reliability.

Ex. 10. What distribution is assumed to be normal in the treatment of the reliability of the mean obtained from a sample? What is the meaning of the term "standard error of the mean"?

Reliability of Other Measures. Formulas similar to the one for σ_M exist for the other measures with which we have worked— the median, the semi-interquartile range, and the standard deviation. Although the *formula for σ_M can be used if the population sampled is any type of distribution* (normal, skewed, U- or J-shaped), *the following formulas hold only if the population sampled is a normal distribution.*

$$\text{Standard error of the median: } \sigma_{Mdn} = \frac{5}{4}\frac{\sigma_s}{\sqrt{N}}$$

$$\text{Standard error of the standard deviation: } \sigma_\sigma = \frac{\sigma_s}{\sqrt{2N}}$$

Standard error of the semi-interquartile range:

$$\sigma_Q = 1.11\frac{\sigma_s}{\sqrt{2N}}$$

or

$$\sigma_Q = 1.65\frac{Q_s}{\sqrt{2N}}$$

The probable error of any measure will be equal to approximately 0.6745 of the standard error, or roughly, two-thirds of the standard error.

By the standard error of the median is meant the *standard deviation of the distribution of medians obtained from all possible samples.* This distribution is assumed to be approximately *normal*, with the true median as mean.

By the standard error of the standard deviation is meant *the standard deviation of the distribution of sigmas obtained from all possible samples.* This distribution is assumed to be approximately *normal*, with the true sigma as mean.

Although it is not usually possible to know definitely whether the entire population being sampled is normal, the nature of a random sample is indicative of the nature of the entire group which it represents. Hence it is fairly safe to apply the above formulas in cases where the sample is approximately normal.

Ex. 11. By analogy with the above definitions state the meaning of the standard error of the semi-interquartile range.

Ex. 12. In an experimental study with 200 children, the results are approximately normal, and

$$
\begin{aligned}
\text{Mean} &= 112.0 \\
\text{Median} &= 111.5 \\
\sigma &= 12.0 \\
Q &= 8.0
\end{aligned}
$$

Find the standard error and the probable error of each of these results (to the nearest tenth). Write each result so as to indicate its reliability, using the form customarily employed in publications.

$$\sigma_M = \frac{\sigma_s}{\sqrt{N}} = \frac{12}{\sqrt{200}} = \frac{12}{10\sqrt{2}} = \frac{6}{5\sqrt{2}} = \frac{6}{10}\sqrt{2} = \frac{3}{5}\sqrt{2} = 0.8$$

$$\sigma_{Mdn} = \frac{5}{4}\frac{\sigma_s}{\sqrt{N}} = \frac{5}{4}\sigma_M = \frac{5}{4}(0.8) = 1.0$$

$$\sigma_\sigma = \frac{12}{\sqrt{400}} = \frac{12}{20} = \frac{3}{5} = 0.6$$

$$\sigma_Q = 1.11\frac{\sigma_s}{\sqrt{2N}} = 1.11\sigma_\sigma = 1.11(0.6) = 0.7$$

or, using the other formula:

$$\sigma_Q = 1.65\frac{Q_s}{\sqrt{2N}} = 1.65\frac{8}{\sqrt{400}} = 1.65(0.4) = 0.7$$

P.E.$_M$ = 0.5	Mean = 112 ± 0.5
P.E.$_{Mdn}$ = 0.7	Median = 111.5 ± 0.7
P.E.$_\sigma$ = 0.4	σ = 12 ± 0.4
P.E.$_Q$ = 0.5	Q = 8 ± 0.5

Ex. 13. One hundred children are given a standardized test. Their scores form an approximately normal distribution. The median score is 70, and $\sigma = 9$. Find limits for the median of the entire group of which the 100 children are a sample. List the median as it would appear in a statistical journal.

Ex. 14. Find the standard errors and the probable errors for the first three σ's listed in Table 46. Assuming that the distributions handled were approximately normal, list these three values of σ in the form

$$\sigma \pm \text{P.E.}_\sigma.$$

Ex. 15. Table 47 furnishes data on the I.Q.'s of East Tennessee mountain children. Assuming that the distributions handled were approximately normal, find σ_{Mdn} and the limits for the true median in each case. Also write each median so as to indicate its reliability, using the form customarily employed in publications. Would you consider the median I.Q. of the 9-year-old children reliable? Explain. Do you think that the median I.Q. of all 10-year-old Tennessee mountain children is approximately 83.4? Explain. Do you think that 80.74 is a fair average of the intelligence of all Tennessee mountain children?

We shall do the work for the first entry in the table. Since the sample is assumed to be approximately normal:

$$Q = \text{P.E.}$$
$$\therefore Q_s = \frac{2}{3}\sigma_s, \text{ approximately}$$

or

$$\sigma_s = \frac{3}{2}Q_s$$
$$\therefore \sigma_s = \frac{3}{2}(11.72) = 17.58$$
$$\sigma_{Mdn} = \frac{5}{4}\frac{\sigma_s}{\sqrt{N}} = \frac{5}{4}\frac{17.58}{\sqrt{564}} = 0.93$$

and the limits for the true median are $80.74 \pm 3(0.93)$ or 77.95 and 83.53.

$$\text{P.E.}_{Mdn} = \frac{2}{3}\sigma_{Mdn} = 0.62$$

and, for a publication, we would write

$$\text{Median} = 80.74 \pm 0.62$$

TABLE 47*

COMPARISON OF I.Q.'s ON ILLINOIS AND DEARBORN TESTS

	Illinois Tests		
	Number of cases	Median I.Q.	Q
Entire group..........	564	80.74	11.72
9-year-olds...........	27	92.5	7.81
10-year-olds.........	63	83.4	10.22
	Dearborn Tests		
Entire group..........	564	81.25	10.62

* Data from "The Intelligence of East Tennessee Mountain Children" by L. R. Wheeler. *Journal of Educational Psychology*, May, 1932.

Ex. 16. Find σ_Q for the first three entries in Table 47.

Let us call attention to the fact that the formulas reveal that *the mean is a more reliable measure of central tendency than the median*, for:

$$\sigma_{Mdn} = \frac{5}{4} \frac{\sigma_s}{\sqrt{N}} = \frac{5}{4}\sigma_M$$

In other words, the standard error of the median is always $\frac{5}{4}$ as large as, or 25 per cent greater than, the standard error of the mean.

Let us also derive another formula to show the reliability of the median for use in exercises like Ex. 15 above. In this exercise it was necessary first to find σ_s before proceeding, since the data give Q and not σ. Hence a formula expressed directly in terms of Q would be useful in this case.

$$\sigma_{Mdn} = \frac{5}{4} \frac{\sigma_s}{\sqrt{N}}$$

Multiplying both sides by $\frac{2}{3}$ we have

$$\frac{2}{3}\sigma_{Mdn} = \frac{5}{4} \frac{\frac{2}{3}\sigma_s}{\sqrt{N}}$$

and hence P.E.$_{Mdn} = \frac{5}{4} \frac{Q_s}{\sqrt{N}}$.

Thus for the first entry in Table 47

$$\text{P.E.}_{Mdn} = \frac{5}{4} \frac{(11.72)}{\sqrt{564}} = 0.62$$

which is the result obtained above by a more laborious method.

Ex. 17. Using the formula P.E.$_{Mdn} = \frac{5}{4} \frac{Q_s}{\sqrt{N}}$, find the probable error of each median in Table 47. Write each median as it would appear in a statistical journal, so as to indicate the reliability.

Ex. 18. In Table 22 find limits for the true median age of rural supervisors in the United States.

Ex. 19. Show that σ is a more reliable measure of variability than Q.

Standard Error of the Difference between Two Means. Suppose that we were to inquire whether the data of Table 46 indicate a real difference between the militarism-pacifism scores of college graduates and college seniors. In other words, are college graduates more inclined toward pacifism than college seniors? Is the difference in means, 0.45, really significant, or is it just due to sampling errors?

If the scores in the two sets, and hence their means, are entirely independent of one another (uncorrelated, as statistics state it), the formula for the *standard error of the difference between two means* is

$$\sigma_d = \sqrt{\sigma_{M_1}^2 + \sigma_{M_2}^2}$$

where σ_{M_1} and σ_{M_2} represent the standard errors of the two means, respectively.

This formula is a special case of a more general formula

$$\sigma_d = \sqrt{\sigma_{M_1}^2 + \sigma_{M_2}^2 - 2r\sigma_{M_1}\sigma_{M_2}}$$

where r is the *correlation* between the sampling errors in the two means (which is the same as the correlation between the two sets of scores).

We shall explain the exact meaning of the term *correlation* in the next chapter. At this point, it will suffice to state that $r = 0$ for *uncorrelated* (independent) scores. Hence the last term under the radical sign will be equal to zero, and the general formula will reduce to the special one.

As an illustration of a difference to which the more general formula would apply, we might take the difference between the mean scores of the same set of students in mathematics and physics. There might be considerable correlation between achievement in mathematics and physics, since students who excel in the one subject very often show similar ability in the other, and those who are deficient in mathematics may also be poor students of physics. In the next chapter, we shall show how r would be computed in this case. After r has been found, the general formula can be used.

Let us apply the special formula to the difference in the mean scores of college graduates and college seniors in Table 46.

$$\sigma_{M_1} = 0.28$$
$$\sigma_{M_2} = 0.23$$

Hence $\sigma_d = \sqrt{0.0784 + 0.0529} = \sqrt{0.1313}$
$$= 0.36$$

Then the limits for the true difference are:

$$0.45 - 3\,(0.36) = -0.63$$
$$0.45 + 3\,(0.36) = 1.53$$

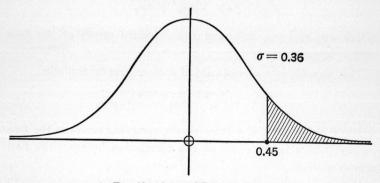

$\sigma = 0.36$

0.45

Fig. 42.—A true difference of zero

Hence we see that the difference may actually be *negative*, that is, college seniors may be more pacifistic, on the average, than college graduates.

What is the probability that college graduates are actually more pacifistic, on the average, than college seniors, in other words, that a difference *greater than zero* exists?

We assume that all the differences which would be obtained from all possible samples would form a normal distribution. See Fig. 42.

The standard deviation of this normal distribution is $\sigma_d = 0.36$.

If the true difference is *zero*, the difference 0.45, of the sample we are handling, would occupy the position in the distribution indicated in Fig. 42.

If the true difference is negative, if, for example, it has the value −0.5, the difference of our sample would occupy a position still further to the right in the distribution. See Fig. 43.

Thus it is evident that if the true difference has any negative value, the difference of our sample will occupy a position somewhere in the base of the shaded area in Fig. 42.

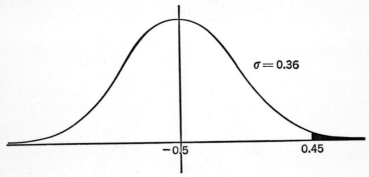

Fig. 43.—A true difference of −0.5

Using the figure, we have

$$\frac{0.45}{0.36} = 1.3\sigma$$

and from Table 44, we find a reading of 0.400, and hence, for the shaded area, we have

$$0.500 - 0.403 = 0.097 = 0.10, \text{ approximately}$$

Hence the probability that the difference of our sample will fall in the base of the shaded area is $\frac{1}{10}$, that is, the probability of a zero or negative true difference is $\frac{1}{10}$.

Thus the probability of a *positive* true difference is $\frac{9}{10}$.

Hence the probability that college graduates, on the average, are actually more pacifistic than college seniors, is $\frac{9}{10}$, and the difference in means, in this case, is fairly reliable.

Ex. 20. In Table 46 find σ_d for the difference in mean scores of juniors and college graduates. What is the probability that college graduates are actually more pacifistic, on the average, than college juniors? Compare the mean scores of sophomores and seniors in the same way.

We shall work out the first part of this exercise.

$$\sigma_{M_1} = \frac{2.16}{\sqrt{83}} = 0.24$$

$$\sigma_{M_2} = \frac{2.05}{\sqrt{96}} = 0.21$$

$$\sigma_d = \sqrt{0.0576 + 0.0441} = 0.32$$

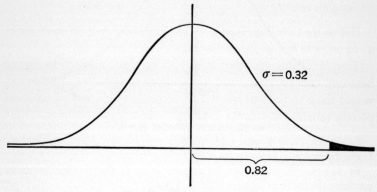

Fig. 44.—Diagram for Ex. 20

If the true difference is zero or negative, the difference of our sample will occupy a position somewhere in the base of the shaded area in Fig. 44.

Now $$\frac{0.82}{0.32} = 2.6\sigma$$

and from Table 44, we find a reading of 0.495, and hence the shaded area is $0.500 - 0.495 = 0.005$.

Hence the probability that the true difference is zero or negative is $\frac{5}{1000}$.

Hence the probability of a positive true difference is $\frac{955}{1000}$, that is, the probability that college graduates are actually more pacifistic, on the average, than college juniors is $\frac{955}{1000}$.

Ex. 21. Using the data of Table 48, find the probability that college sophomores, on the average, really exceed college freshmen in intelligence.

We might ask how large a difference in means should be, in order to be *completely reliable*.

The limits for a true difference are

$$D_s \pm 3\sigma_d$$

where D_s = the difference of the sample.

If the difference of the sample is completely reliable, the lower limit for the true difference *cannot be negative*. At worst, it can be equal to zero.

$$D_s - 3\sigma_d = 0$$

yields

$$D_s = 3\sigma_d \text{ (at least)}$$

for complete reliability.

Hence we may say that a *difference should be 3 or more times* σ_d *in order to be completely reliable.*

Thus, in Table 46, since $\sigma_d = 0.36$ for the difference in means between college graduates and college seniors, the difference would have to be $3 (0.36) = 1.08$ or greater in order to be completely reliable.

Ex. 22. In Table 46 find σ_d for college sophomores and college juniors. Is the difference in mean scores completely reliable?

Ex. 23. Do you think that college graduates, on the average, are more pacifistic than college sophomores? Give proof.

Standard Error of the Difference between Two Medians. For two medians:

$$\sigma_d = \sqrt{\sigma_{Mdn_1}^2 + \sigma_{Mdn_2}^2 - 2r\sigma_{Mdn_1}\sigma_{Mdn_2}}$$

where r = the correlation between the sampling errors in the two medians.

Ex. 24. For two groups, the scores are entirely independent, and the data are as follows:

Group	Median	N	σ
A	70	100	10
B	69	225	12

Find the probability that the median of the entire group of which A is a sample actually exceeds the median of the group of which B is a sample. What difference in medians would be completely reliable?

Ex. 25. Using the data of Table 47, find σ_d for the difference in median

I.Q.'s of the entire group in the Illinois and Dearborn tests. What is the probability that the median I.Q. of all the children of whom these 564 are a sample is actually higher on the Dearborn tests than on the Illinois tests?

Ex. 26. Using Table 47, find σ_d for the difference in median I.Q.'s of 9 and 10-year-olds in the Illinois tests. Is this difference completely reliable?

Ex. 27. In Table 48 find the standard error of each mean and each σ listed under the heading Sophomores. List each mean and σ in the forms Mean $\pm$ P.E.$_M$ and $\sigma \pm$ P.E.$_\sigma$, respectively.

Find also σ_d for the difference in mean intelligence between freshmen and sophomores. Is this difference completely reliable?

Find also σ_d for the differences in mean scores in English; in English and general culture; in general science. Are these differences completely reliable? Are they fairly reliable? Give proof.

TABLE 48

COMPARISON OF FRESHMEN AND SOPHOMORES FROM SEVEN COLLEGES IN VARIOUS TESTS*

	Freshmen N = 298		Sophomores N = 817	
	Mean	Sigma	Mean	Sigma
Intelligence....................	53.8	9.4	54.6	9.7
Grammar......................	30.5	8.0	27.9	9.0
English.......................	221.5	52.6	209.0	54.1
English and general culture.....	425.2	125.7	391.7	118.7
General science...............	68.0	29.2	83.1	36.3

* The Educational Record—Vol. 13, No. 4, Oct., 1932. "The 1932 College Sophomore Testing Program." A Report by the Advisory Committee in College Testing.

Standard Error of Any Difference. We might here remark that the *standard error of the difference between any two measures of the same type* has the same form as the standard error of the differences we have treated.

Thus, for the difference between two sigmas:

$$\sigma_d = \sqrt{\sigma_{\sigma_1}^2 + \sigma_{\sigma_2}^2 - 2r\sigma_{\sigma_1}\sigma_{\sigma_2}}$$

If the two groups of scores are entirely independent,

$$\sigma_d = \sqrt{\sigma_{\sigma_1}^2 + \sigma_{\sigma_2}^2}$$

Ex. 28. Write the general formula for the standard error of the difference between two Q's. Write the special formula in case the two sets of scores are entirely independent.

Note that the *standard error of the difference between any two measures of the same type* is

$$\sigma_d = \sqrt{\sigma_1{}^2 + \sigma_2{}^2 - 2r\sigma_1\sigma_2}$$

where σ_1 = the standard error of the first measure.

σ_2 = the standard error of the second measure.

r = the correlation between the sampling errors of the two measures.

Ex. 29. In Table 49 verify the entries for σ_d in σ's, σ_d in Q's, and chances in one hundred that the true difference is above zero. Which differences are completely reliable? Which differences are definitely unreliable? What general conclusion can you draw from the data of this article?

Ex. 30. Explain the first quotation in the introduction to this book.

Summary. In this chapter we have dealt with the question of sampling errors and employed in this connection the following formulas:

$$\sigma_M = \frac{\sigma_s}{\sqrt{N}}$$

$$\sigma_{Mdn} = \frac{5}{4}\frac{\sigma_s}{\sqrt{N}}$$

$$\sigma_\sigma = \frac{\sigma_s}{\sqrt{2N}}$$

$$\sigma_Q = 1.11\frac{\sigma_s}{\sqrt{2N}} \text{ or } \sigma_Q = 1.65\frac{Q_s}{\sqrt{2N}}$$

$$\text{P.E.}_{Mdn} = \frac{5}{4}\frac{Q_s}{\sqrt{N}}$$

$$\sigma_d = \sqrt{\sigma_1{}^2 + \sigma_2{}^2 - 2r\sigma_1\sigma_2}$$

where σ_1 = the standard error of the first measure.

σ_2 = the standard error of the second measure.

r = the correlation between the sampling errors of the two measures.

TABLE 49*

SEX DIFFERENCES IN THE VARIABILITY OF A SAMPLE OF 482 GIRLS AND A SAMPLE OF 464 BOYS IN SEVERAL SCHOOL SUBJECTS AND IN COMPOSITE SCORE FOR ALL SCHOOL SUBJECTS

		σ	σ_d in σ's	Chances in 100 true difference is above zero	Q	σ_d in Q's	Chances in 100 true difference is above zero
Composite score	Girls	12.39			7.67		
	Boys	13.20			9.30		
	Difference	−.81	0.59	91	−1.63	0.66	99
Reading	Girls	36.51			24.23		
	Boys	38.37			25.72		
	Difference	−1.86	1.72	86	−1.49	1.91	78
Arithmetic	Girls	37.07			24.47		
	Boys	37.64			23.69		
	Difference	−.57	1.72	63	.78	1.52	70
Nature study and science	Girls	15.15			9.81		
	Boys	16.05			10.72		
	Difference	−.90	0.72	89	−.91	0.78	88
History and literature	Girls	13.50			8.64		
	Boys	17.90			12.27		
	Difference	−4.60	0.73	100	−3.63	0.81	100

* "Sex Differences in Intellectual Abilities" by J. D. Heilman, *Journal of Educational Psychology*, January, 1933.

REVIEW QUESTIONS

Ex. 31. As an application of the material of this chapter we present for analysis part of a table from "The Achievement of Gifted Children Enrolled and Not Enrolled in Special Opportunity Classes" by Howard A. Gay and Leta S. Hollingworth, *Journal of Educational Research*, November, 1931.

This article presents the results of a study of the comparative achievement of two groups of exceptional children. One of these groups was segregated and given special instruction while the pupils of the other group were mixed in the usual manner among heterogeneously composed classes. After three years of experimentation, the Stanford Achievement Tests were given to both groups. E.Q.'s for each individual were found by dividing the educational age (determined by reference to age norms for 1922 edition of the Stanford Achievement Test) by the chronological age. A.Q.'s were found by finding the ratio between the I.Q. (Stanford-Binet) and the E.Q.

TABLE 50

MEAN EDUCATIONAL AND ACHIEVEMENT QUOTIENTS OF 92 BRIGHT CHILDREN
ENROLLED AND NOT ENROLLED IN SPECIAL OPPORTUNITY CLASSES

Standard Achievement Test	Regular class group N =36		Opportunity class group N =56		Difference		Difference	
	Mean E.Q.	Mean A.Q.	Mean E.Q.	Mean A.Q.	E.Q.	P.E._d	A.Q.	P.E._d
Total reading score	151.9±1.0	102.4±1.1	152.0±1.2	97.0±1.2	0.1	1.56	5.4	1.63
Total arithmetic score	153.2±2.0	100.4±1.4	156.1±1.2	100.7±0.9	2.9	2.33	0.3	1.66
Nature study	145.0±1.7	98.5±1.1	144.3±1.2	92.9±0.8	0.7	2.08	5.6	1.36
History and literature	152.5±1.3	100.3±1.1	155.8±0.9	100.4±1.1	3.3	1.58	0.1	1.56
Language usage	148.7±2.2	100.3±1.3	147.5±1.4	96.1±0.9	1.2	2.60	4.2	1.58
Dictation	149.3±1.4	100.8±1.3	153.5±1.0	99.8±0.8	4.2	1.72	1.0	1.53
Composite score	150.5±1.6	99.7±1.1	153.0±1.1	99.1±0.7	2.5	1.94	0.6	1.30

(a) In Table 50 compare the mean E.Q. of the two groups in each subject. Are the differences in nature study and language reliable? What data in the table show this fact?

(b) In Table 50 compare the mean A.Q. of the two groups in each subject. Compare also the composite A.Q.'s. Are these differences fairly reliable? Are any of the differences completely reliable?

(c) Do you agree with the following conclusion reached by the authors of this article? "There is no appreciable effect upon standardized accomplishment, of the extra work done by the segregated group, save possibly in the cases of nature study and reading. . . . It is true that in nine of the eleven school subjects mentioned, the pupils in regular classes average a little higher in A.Q. . . . The differences in amount, however, are insignificant. . . . Thus, though covering a large amount of intellectual work *in addition to that performed by the pupils in regular classes*, the segregated pupils show no deficit in the achievements measured by the Stanford Achievement Test."

(d) Which means in the table are most reliable? least reliable?

(e) Find limits for the mean E.Q. in arithmetic of all the children of whom the group of 36 are a sample. Find limits for the mean A.Q. in dictation of all the children of whom the 56 are a sample.

Ex. 32. Mark the following statements *true* or *false*.

(1) The formula for the standard error of the mean may be applied to normal samples only.

(2) The formula for the standard error of the standard deviation may be applied to normal samples only.

(3) The use of all the formulas for standard errors implies the assumption that the distribution of measures from all possible samples is approximately a normal one.

(4) The greater the variability of a sample, the more reliable the mean obtained from it.

(5) The greater the number of cases in a sample, the more reliable the median obtained from it.

(6) Doubling the number of cases in a sample will make the standard error of estimate in the mean one-half as great, providing that the σ of the sample remains the same.

(7) Multiplying the number of cases in a sample by 4 will make the standard error of the standard deviation half as great, providing that the σ of the sample remains the same.

Ex. 33. Bring in illustrative material from educational periodicals showing the use of the formulas for the reliability of measures.

CHAPTER VII

CORRELATION AND CURVE-FITTING

Correlation. One important need for statistical procedure in modern education is in the classification of pupils. Can we predict from an intelligence test whether a student is good high-school material, whether he will be proficient in mathematics, whether he is capable of studying modern languages? If a student shows weakness in second-year high-school mathematics, should he be debarred from electing science in his third year? If he has ability in English composition, is there any reason to believe that he will be a strong history student? The statistical methods treated in this chapter are associated with the answering of questions of this type.

Table 51 lists the scores obtained by 20 junior-college students of advanced science in two tests, one designed to measure reasoning ability, the other to measure knowledge of facts. Do the students who have high ratings in the judgment test also have high ratings in the fact test? Do the same students have low ratings in both tests? Judging by these scores, does there seem to be any relation between knowledge of facts and ability to reason?

If the *correspondence*, or *correlation*, as it is called, between knowledge of facts and ability to reason were *perfect*, each student would occupy the same relative position in the fact test scores as in the judgment test scores, that is, the student with the highest rating in one test would have the highest rating in the other; the student who stood second in one test would stand second in the other, etc.

Table 52 gives a list of hypothetical marks in French and Latin to illustrate this situation. This table illustrates *perfect rank correlation*.

133

TABLE 51*

SCORES IN TWO TESTS OF JUNIOR-COLLEGE STUDENTS
STUDYING ADVANCED SCIENCE

Student	Score in judg-ment test	Score in fact test
1	83	88
2	79	82
3	77	90
4	76	84
5	75	85
6	75	82
7	72	86
8	72	74
9	70	84
10	70	79
11	69	79
12	69	78
13	66	78
14	65	72
15	64	69
16	63	65
17	63	73
18	59	50
19	58	75
20	49	50

* Data from "A Study of Scientific Attitudes as Related to Factual Knowledge," by Evelyn B. Moore, *School Review*, May, 1930.

The correlation is not absolutely perfect since, for example, a change of 2 from the first to the second mark in French corresponds to a change of 4 in the Latin marks, whereas a change of 2 from the second to the third French mark corresponds to a change of only 2 in the Latin. The ratio of the change in Latin mark to the change in French is 2 in the first case, and 1 in the second case. Proceeding to the next pair of marks the ratio is $\frac{2}{3}$, etc.

Now to have absolutely perfect correlation the ratio of the differences between consecutive pairs of scores should always be the same. Table 53 is an hypothetical illustration of absolutely *perfect correlation*. The ratio of the changes in going from the first pair of marks to the second is $\frac{3}{5}$. In going from the second to the third this ratio is $\frac{6}{10} = \frac{3}{5}$. In going from the sixth to the seventh the ratio is $\frac{9}{15} = \frac{3}{5}$.

TABLE 52

PERFECT RANK CORRELATION AS ILLUSTRATED BY FRENCH
AND LATIN MARKS OF 10 HYPOTHETICAL STUDENTS

Student	French mark	Latin mark
1	95	90
2	93	86
3	91	84
4	85	80
5	81	77
6	75	75
7	70	72
8	67	68
9	60	66
10	55	63

TABLE 53

PERFECT CORRELATION AS ILLUSTRATED BY FRENCH AND
LATIN MARKS OF 10 HYPOTHETICAL STUDENTS

Student	French mark	Latin mark
1	95	90
2	90	87
3	80	81
4	75	78
5	70	75
6	65	72
7	50	63
8	45	60
9	40	57
10	30	51

Table 54 is an hypothetical illustration of *perfect negative correlation*. In the case of negative correlation, the student who stands first in one set of scores stands last in the other set. The second student in one set ranks next to the last in the other, etc.

Since absolutely perfect correlation occurs only in hypothetical illustrations, some way is needed to determine whether correlation is *high* or *low*. Correlation is *high and positive* if, in general, a high rank in one set of scores means a high rank in the other, and a low rank in one set means a low rank in the other; Tables 20 and 51 illustrate this type of correlation. *High negative* correlation exists if, in general, a high rank in one set of scores corresponds to a low rank in the other, and if a low rank in the first set corresponds to a high rank in the other.

Correlation is *low* if no sort of correspondence seems to exist, if a high score in one set is just as likely to correspond to a low

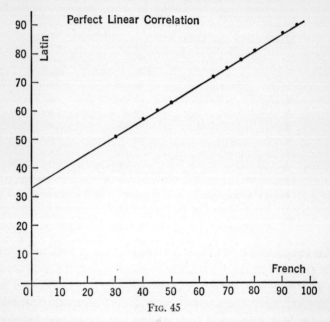

FIG. 45

score in the other set as to a high score. Table 60 illustrates this type of correlation.

To measure correlation in more exact fashion, mathematical treatment is necessary. We shall, in the subsequent pages, give an elementary mathematical discussion of this subject.

In Fig. 45 the data of Table 53 have been graphed. Scores in French have been laid off on the X axis, and scores in Latin on the Y axis. Each point thus represents the pair of scores for one student. We see that these points lie on a *straight line*. Thus Fig. 45 gives a picture of *perfect linear correlation*. A set of points like those in the figure might, however, lie exactly on some other type of curve. In that case we would have perfect *curvilinear* correlation. Approximate linear correlation is the type of correlation which is most frequently assumed in educational measurement. Hence we shall treat the question of linear correlation first and more fully, and postpone the question of curvilinear correlation for another chapter.

TABLE 54

PERFECT NEGATIVE CORRELATION AS ILLUSTRATED BY THE
MATHEMATICS AND ENGLISH MARKS OF 10 HYPOTHETICAL
STUDENTS

Student	Mathematics mark	English mark
1................................	95	57
2................................	90	60
3................................	80	66
4................................	75	69
5................................	70	72
6................................	65	75
7................................	60	78
8................................	55	81
9................................	50	84
10................................	40	90

An examination of Table 51 shows that it exhibits a fairly high correlation between scientific knowledge (as measured by the fact test) and reasoning ability (as measured by the judgment test), since there seems, in general, to be a correspondence between high scores and high scores, low scores and low scores. These data have been plotted in Fig. 46. Although the points do not lie exactly on a straight line, their trend can be described fairly well by the straight line drawn in the figure. Again, the trend of a set of points might be described by some other type of curve.

Curve-Fitting. From the statistical point of view it is hardly correct to come to any conclusion as to the existence of high or low correlation unless the number of cases is large, at least 25, say. We shall show later on, moreover, that the greater the number of cases, the more reliable are the conclusions drawn. Now, if the number of cases is large, it would be rather difficult to determine the "trend" line or curve in a figure like Fig. 46. In order to make the process of "fitting" a curve to a set of points a more exact matter, and at the same time to give a more precise definition of correlation, we introduce the subject of curve-fitting. A complete treatment of the theory of curve-fitting is naturally beyond the scope of this work. We shall, how-

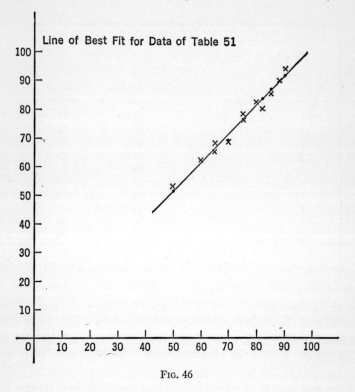

FIG. 46

ever, consider a few of the most elementary facts of this theory in order to help us understand some of the important applications to educational statistics.

Table 55 gives the results obtained by a student in a physics experiment to study the relationship between resistance and current in an electrical circuit. In the experiment, the electromotive force was kept at 110 volts, the resistance in the circuit was varied, and the corresponding effect on the current studied. In Fig. 47 the results are represented graphically. Each set of values in the table is represented by a cross. Since it was not possible to draw a smooth curve so that all the points would lie exactly on it, a smooth curve has been drawn so as to describe the general trend of the points. The actual points representing the data have been moved up or down. We say that they have

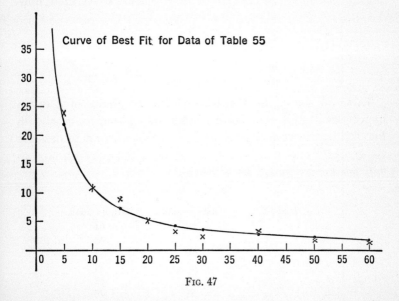

Fig. 47

been "graduated" so as to fall on the curve. In Fig. 47 the position of the graduated points is indicated by dots, unless these points coincide with the original ones, as in the case of (10, 11) and (20, 5.5).

TABLE 55

R Resistance in ohms	I Current in amperes
5	23
10	11
15	9
20	5.5
25	3.5
30	2.5
40	3.5
50	2
60	1.5

Ex. 1. Using Fig. 47, fill in the following table:

R Resistance in ohms	I Graduated value of current in amperes
5	22
10	11
15	7.3
20	
25	
30	
40	
50	
60	

Table 56 shows the English and history grades of a dozen hypothetical students. These results are plotted as crosses in Fig. 48. In this case, a straight line has been drawn to describe the general trend of these results. Again, dots have been used to indicate the graduated set of marks.

TABLE 56

Student	English mark	History mark
1	90	94
2	88	90
3	85	85
4	82	80
5	80	82
6	75	78
7	75	76
8	70	68
9	65	68
10	65	65
11	60	62
12	50	53

Ex. 2. Make a table of the graduated set of marks in Fig. 48.

The Method of Moments. There are a number of methods of curve-fitting. We shall treat one of these briefly, namely, the method of moments.[1]

If we have a point with coordinates (X, Y) we shall call:

XY the first moment with respect to the Y axis

X^2Y the second moment with respect to the Y axis

[1] A brief treatment of another method, the method of least squares, will be found in Note III of the Appendix.

X^3Y the third moment with respect to the Y axis

....

X^nY the nth moment with respect to the Y axis

Note that $X^0Y = Y$ will be the zeroth moment with respect to the Y axis. Thus, for the point $(2, 3)$:

The zeroth moment $= 2^0 \cdot 3 = 3$
The 1st moment $\quad = 2^1 \cdot 3 = 6$
The 2nd moment $\quad = 2^2 \cdot 3 = 12$
The 3rd moment $\quad = 2^3 \cdot 3 = 24$

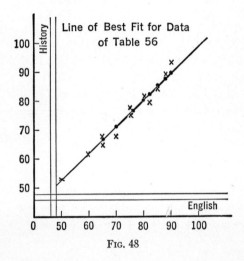

FIG. 48

If we have a set of points, the moment of this set is defined as the sum of the moments of the individual points. For example, if the set of points be $(1, 2)$, $(2, -1)$, $(3, 5)$:

The zeroth moment of the set $= 2 - 1 + 5 = 6$
The 1st moment of the set $= (1)(2) + (2)(-1) + (3)(5) = 15$
The 2nd moment of the set $= (1)(2) + (4)(-1) + (9)(5) = 43$
The 3rd moment of the set $= (1)(2) + (8)(-1) + (27)(5) = 129$

Now suppose that it is required to fit a straight line to the set of points $(1, 3)$, $(2, 2)$, $(3, 4)$, $(4, 6)$, $(5, 5)$. (See Fig. 49.)

Let the equation of this line be $Y = mX + b$, where m and b are constants which we are to determine.

Now curve-fitting by the method of moments employs the following procedure. *The moments of the set of given points are equated to the moments of the set of graduated points.*

TABLE 57

Given points		Graduated points	
X	Y	X	Y
1	3	1	$m + b$
2	2	2	$2m + b$
3	4	3	$3m + b$
4	6	4	$4m + b$
5	5	5	$5m + b$

In Table 57 we have listed the coordinates of the graduated points. These were obtained by using the fact that when a point is graduated, it moves up or down, but its x coordinate or abscissa remains the same. The abscissa of the first graduated point is 1. Since the point lies on the line $Y = mX + b$, we substitute $X = 1$ in this equation to find $y = m(1) + b = m + b$.

For $X = 2$, $Y = m(2) + b = 2m + b$, etc.

Next we have:

Zeroth moment of the set $= 3 + 2 + 4 + 6 + 5 = 20$
Zeroth moment of the graduated set $= m + b + 2m$
$+ b + 3m + b + 4m + b + 5m + b = 15m + 5b$

Equating these two, $15m + 5b = 20$
Next:

1st moment of the given set $= 3 + 4 + 12 + 24 + 25 = 68$
1st moment of the graduated set $= 1(m + b) + 2(2m + b)$
$+ 3(3m + b) + 4(4m + b) + 5(5m + b) = 55m + 15b$
and

$$55m + 15b = 68$$

Thus we have two unknowns, m and b, and two equations, which, in general, should be sufficient to determine m and b.

$$(1) \quad 15m + 5b = 20$$
$$(2) \quad 55m + 15b = 68$$

Multiplying (1) by 3 we have:

$$\begin{array}{ll}
(3) & 45m + 15b = 60 \\
(2) & 55m + 15b = 68
\end{array}$$

Subtracting (3) from (2) we have:

$$10m = 8$$
$$m = 0.8$$

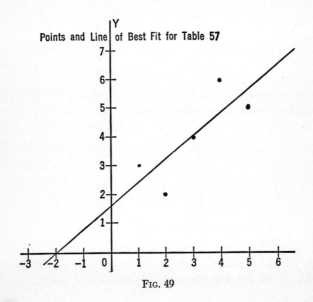

Points and Line of Best Fit for Table 57

Fig. 49

Dividing (1) by 5 to simplify it and substituting $m = 0.8$ we have:

$$3(0.8) + b = 4$$
$$2.4 + b = 4$$
$$b = 1.6$$

The equation of the line of best fit is then:

$$Y = 0.8X + 1.6$$

The set of given points and this line of best fit have been drawn in Fig. 49.

Ex. 3. Find the line of best fit, $Y = mX + b$, for the set of points $(-1, 2)$, $(0, 4)$, $(1, 3)$, $(2, 6)$, $(3, 6)$. Plot the points and the line of best fit.

Ex. 4. Find the line of best fit $Y = mX + b$, for the set of points $(-2, -6)$, $(-1, -2)$, $(1, 3)$, $(2, 7)$, $(3, 8)$. Plot the points and the line of best fit.

Ex. 5. Find the line of best fit $Y = mX + b$, for the set of points $(-1, 1)$, $(1, 5)$, $(2, 6)$, $(3, 7)$, $(4, 12)$.

Ex. 6. The grades of 7 students in mathematics and Latin are as follows:

Mathematics	Latin
A	A
A	B
B	B
C	B
C	C
D	B
D	C

Calling mathematics X and Latin Y, A = 3, B = 2, C = 1, D = 0, the table can be rewritten as we have indicated.

X	Y
3	3
3	2
2	2
1	2
1	1
0	2
0	1

Find the line $Y = mX + b$ of best fit for this set of scores.

Ex. 7. Fit the curve $Y = aX^2 + b$ to the set of points $(0, 1)$, $(1, 3)$, $(2, 7)$, $(3, 10)$, $(4, 19)$. Plot the points and the curve of best fit.

We have assumed, in most of the examples given above, that the run of points was best described by a straight line, $Y = mX + b$. This, of course, need not be the case. If we were to proceed further in the theory of curve-fitting we could tell whether the curve of best fit for a set of points is a straight line or some other type of curve, and, in the latter case, we would have criteria for judging what particular type of curve to use.

Let us call attention to an important fact connected with the line of best fit.

In Table 57 the mean of the X's

$$M_x = \frac{1 + 2 + 3 + 4 + 5}{5} = 3$$

and the mean of the Y's

$$M_y = \frac{3+2+4+6+5}{5} = 4$$

We have found the line of best fit to be

$$Y = 0.8X + 1.6$$

Let us show that the point $(3, 4)$ lies on this line.

$$4 \overset{?}{=} 0.8\ (3) + 1.6$$
$$4 \overset{?}{=} 2.4 + 1.6$$
$$4 = 4$$

We have verified in this particular case a fact which can be proved to be true in general, namely, that *the point whose co-ordinates are the mean of the X's and the mean of the Y's lies on the line of best fit.*

Ex. 8. Verify in Exs. 3, 4, 5, and 6 that the points whose coordinates are the mean of the X's and the mean of the Y's lie on the lines of best fit.

Now it is customary, in statistical work, to move the origin to the special point (M_x, M_y), keeping the axes parallel to their original position.

We have seen, in the chapter on graphs, that if a straight line passes through the origin, its equation is of specially simple form, since it lacks the constant term.

Let us use the illustrative example above to see how such a change in the position of the coordinate axes would affect the coordinates of points. In this example

$$(M_x, M_y) = (3, 4)$$

Let us use this point as origin. From Fig. 50 we see that in this new coordinate system $(1, 3)$ becomes $(-2, -1)$, $(2, 2)$ becomes $(-1, -2)$, $(3, 4)$ becomes $(0, 0)$, $(4, 6)$ becomes $(1, 2)$, etc. We see that the new values of X and Y can be obtained by subtracting 3 from the old values of X and 4 from the old values of Y.

In other words the new X's are the *deviations of the original X's from the mean of the X's* and the new Y's are the *deviations of the original Y's from the mean of the Y's.* We have as the table of the new coordinates:

New X	New Y
−2	−1
−1	−2
0	0
1	2
2	1

We shall use *small letters* for the *new* X and Y. Thus x = new X, y = new Y. In other words, x and y represent the *deviations*

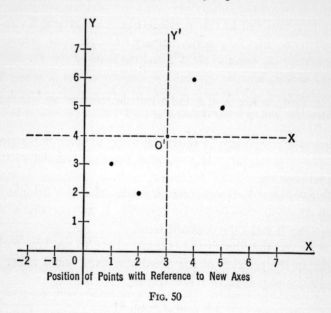

Position of Points with Reference to New Axes

FIG. 50

from the mean of the X's and the mean of the Y's, respectively. Thus we have:

x	y
−2	−1
−1	−2
0	0
1	2
2	1

Correlation Coefficient. As we have just seen, if (M_x, M_y) is used as the origin, the line of best fit will be of the specially simple form

$$y = mx$$

where x and y (deviations from M_x and M_y, respectively) are the new coordinates.

Now mathematical theory[1] shows m to have the form

$$m = r\frac{\sigma_y}{\sigma_x}$$

where r is called the correlation coefficient and has the value

$$r = \frac{\Sigma xy}{\sqrt{\Sigma x^2 \Sigma y^2}}$$

and σ_x and σ_y are the standard deviations of the X's and Y's respectively.

Thus, the line of best fit has the form

$$y = r\frac{\sigma_y}{\sigma_x}x$$

Ex. 9. Using the formula just quoted, find the correlation coefficient and the line of best fit for the set of points in Ex. 3.

X	Y	x	y	x^2	y^2	xy
−1	2	−2	−2.2	4	4.84	4.4
0	4	−1	−0.2	1	0.04	0.2
1	3	0	−1.2	0	1.44	0
2	6	1	1.8	1	3.24	1.8
3	6	2	1.8	4	3.24	3.6

$M_x = 1$ $M_y = 4.2$ $\Sigma x^2 = 10$ $\Sigma y^2 = 12.80$ $\Sigma xy = 10.0$

$$r = \frac{\Sigma xy}{\sqrt{\Sigma x^2 \Sigma y^2}} = \frac{10}{\sqrt{(10)(12.8)}} = 0.9$$

Now, in our work, x represents deviation from the mean of the X's, M_x. Hence the standard deviation of the X's can be written

$$\sigma_x = \sqrt{\frac{\Sigma x^2}{N}}$$

[1] A proof of this fact is given in Note IV of the Appendix.

and similarly,

$$\sigma_y = \sqrt{\frac{\Sigma y^2}{N}}$$

In our example,

$$\sigma_x = \sqrt{\frac{10}{5}} = 1.4$$

$$\sigma_y = \sqrt{\frac{12.8}{5}} = 1.6$$

The line of best fit will be

$$y = r\frac{\sigma_y}{\sigma_x}x$$
$$y = (0.9)\left(\frac{1.6}{1.4}\right)x$$
$$y = 1.0x, \text{ approximately}$$

Ex. 10. Find the correlation coefficient and the line of best fit with (M_x, M_y) as origin, using the formula:

$$y = r\frac{\sigma_y}{\sigma_x}x$$

for the set of points in Ex. 4.

Ex. 11. Show that the correlation coefficient for the set of scores in Table 53 is 1. (It can be proved that $r = 1$ in all cases of perfect positive correlation.) Find also the line of best fit.

Student	French mark (X)	Latin mark (Y)	x	y	x^2	y^2	xy
1	95	90	31	19	961	361	589
2	90	87	26	16	676	256	416
3	80	81	16	10	256	100	160
4	75	78	11	7	121	49	77
5	70	75	6	4	36	16	24
6	65	72	1	1	1	1	1
7	50	63	−14	−8	196	64	112
8	45	60	−19	−11	361	121	209
9	40	57	−24	−14	376	196	336
10	30	51	−34	−20	1156	400	680

$$\Sigma x^2 = 4340 \quad \Sigma y^2 = 1564 \quad \Sigma xy = 2604$$

$M_x = 64$; $M_y = 71$, to the nearest unit

$$r = \frac{\Sigma xy}{\sqrt{\Sigma x^2 \Sigma y^2}} = \frac{2604}{\sqrt{(4340)(1564)}} = \frac{2604}{2605} = 1, \text{ approximately}$$

$$\sigma_y = \sqrt{\frac{\Sigma y^2}{N}} = \sqrt{\frac{1564}{10}} = 12.5$$

$$\sigma_x = \sqrt{\frac{\Sigma x^2}{N}} = \sqrt{\frac{4340}{10}} = 20.8$$

Line of best fit is

$$y = r\frac{\sigma_y}{\sigma_x}x$$

$$y = \frac{12.5}{20.8}x$$

$$y = 0.6x$$

Ex. 12. Show that $r = -1$ for the set of scores in Table 54. (It can be proved that $r = -1$ whenever perfect negative correlation exists.)

Ex. 13. Find r for the data of Table 51.

Ex. 14. The correlation in a certain study, between history scores (X) and English scores (Y), is 0.7. The mean of the history scores (M_x) is 75 with a standard deviation (σ_x) of 7; the mean of the English scores (M_y) is 71 with a standard deviation (σ_y) of 6. Find the line of best fit with (M_x, M_y) as origin. Using the equation of this line of best fit predict the English mark of a student whose history mark is 85; whose history mark is 60.

Line of best fit $y = 0.7\frac{6}{7}x$

$$y = 0.6x$$

Remember that the x and y in this equation are not the original history and English scores but the deviations of these scores from their respective means.

Hence for the student whose history mark is 85, $x = 85 - 75 = 10$.

Substituting this in the line of best fit, we have

$$y = 0.6 \, (10) = 6$$

This is the deviation of the corresponding English mark from its mean. Hence the English mark is $71 + 6 = 77$.

For the student whose history mark is 60

$$x = 60 - 75 = -15$$

Substituting this in the line of best fit, we have $y = (0.6)(-15) = -9$. Hence the corresponding English mark is

$$71 - 9 = 62$$

Ex. 15. In a certain study, the correlation between achievement in algebra (X) and geometry (Y) is 0.8. The mean achievement in algebra is 69 with a σ of 9, and the mean achievement in geometry is 60 with a σ of 11. Find the line of best fit with (M_x, M_y) as origin. Using the equation of this line of best fit, predict the geometry mark of a student whose algebra mark is 85; whose algebra mark is 60.

NOTE: Remember that the predictions made in Exs. 14 and 15 are based on the *assumption* that the point whose coordinates are represented by a pair of English and history marks or by a pair of algebra and geometry marks will lie on the line of best fit. We know that not all the points lie exactly on this line, but all do lie fairly close to it, so that the predictions are approximate. The line of best fit gives the *most probable* value of y corresponding to a given x.

The Regression Lines. Now, in the above work, we have used the theory of moments about the Y axis and have assumed that the line of best fit was of the form $Y = mX + b$. We have used the equation obtained, namely, $y = r\dfrac{\sigma_y}{\sigma_x}x$, to predict Y scores when the X scores were known. Now it is customary in statistical work to obtain another line of best fit by assuming this line to be of the form $X = nY + a$ and to use this other equation to predict X scores when Y scores are known. This other equation is derived by the use of moments about the X axis. The definitions and treatments for such work are entirely analogous to the handling of moments about the Y axis, and the equation of the line of best fit, with (M_x, M_y) as origin, is:

$$x = r\frac{\sigma_x}{\sigma_y}y$$

The two lines of best fit are known as *regression lines*. The name *regression* comes from the fact that Sir Francis Galton first introduced the term in the case of inheritance of stature. His study revealed that the sons of tall fathers were not in general as tall as the fathers, that is, that they step back or "regress" toward the height of the average man.

$$y = r\frac{\sigma_y}{\sigma_x}x$$

is said to give the *regression of* y *on* x and is used to *predict* y *when* x *is known.*

$$x = r\frac{\sigma_x}{\sigma_y}y$$

is said to give the *regression of* x *on* y and is used to *predict* x *when* y *is known.*

Ex. 16. Write the equation giving the regression of x on y, using the data of Ex. 14. Use them to estimate the history mark of a student whose English mark is 65.

$$x = 0.7\frac{7}{6}y$$
$$x = 0.8y$$
$$y = 65 - 71 = -6$$
$$x = 0.8(-6) = -4.8$$

History mark = $75 - 4.8 = 70.2 = 70$, approximately.

Ex. 17. Write the equation giving the regression of x on y using the data of Ex. 15. Use them to estimate the algebra mark of a student whose geometry mark is 90; whose geometry mark is 50.

Ex. 18. Using the results of Ex. 11, write the regression equations. Estimate the Latin mark of a student whose French mark is 78. Estimate the French mark of a student whose Latin mark is 55.

Ex. 19. Write the regression equations using your results for Ex. 13. Estimate the score in the fact test obtained by a student whose rating in the judgment test is 55. Estimate the score in the judgment test of a student whose rating in the fact test is 92.

Mathematical Meaning of a Correlation Coefficient. Let us change the form of the equation of the regression line

$$y = r\frac{\sigma_y}{\sigma_x}x$$

by dividing both sides by σ_y. Then

$$\frac{y}{\sigma_y} = r\frac{x}{\sigma_x}$$

or

$$\frac{\dfrac{y}{\sigma_y}}{\dfrac{x}{\sigma_x}} = r$$

Since (M_x, M_y) is the origin, we have seen above that x and y represent deviations from their respective means. In Chapter III we have defined a standard score as $\dfrac{x}{\sigma}$ where x represents deviation from the mean. Hence $\dfrac{y}{\sigma_y}$ and $\dfrac{x}{\sigma_x}$ represent standard scores, and r is the *ratio of these standard scores*. This ratio is called the *correlation coefficient*. We have here, then, the *mathematical* meaning of correlation.

It must be remembered that these standard scores come from the regression equations and hence do not represent an actual pair of scores obtained from empirical data. $\frac{y}{\sigma_y}$ is the *most probable standard score* (as predicted from the regression equation), corresponding to a *given standard score* $\frac{x}{\sigma_x}$.

In the same way, we obtain from the other regression equation:

$$\frac{\dfrac{x}{\sigma_x}}{\dfrac{y}{\sigma_y}} = r$$

In this case $\frac{x}{\sigma_x}$ is the most probable standard score (as predicted from the regression equation), corresponding to a given standard score $\frac{y}{\sigma_y}$.

Values of r. It can be proved mathematically that the correlation coefficient r can never have a value numerically greater than 1, that is, that the values which it can have lie between -1 and $+1$. $r = +1$ represents *perfect positive correlation*, and $r = -1$ represents *perfect negative correlation*, as we have seen above.

Let us refer once more to the meaning derived above for a correlation coefficient. There we found that

$$\frac{\dfrac{y}{\sigma_y}}{\dfrac{x}{\sigma_x}} = r$$

that is, that r is the ratio of the two corresponding standard scores (as *determined from the regression equation*).

If $r = 1$, that is, for *perfect positive correlation*, we have:

$$\frac{\dfrac{y}{\sigma_y}}{\dfrac{x}{\sigma_x}} = 1$$

Thus the two standard scores, the predicted and the given, are always equal.

If $r = -1$, that is, for *perfect negative correlation*, the standard scores are equal numerically, but opposite in sign.

Perfect correlation is naturally not to be expected in educational data. *When* r *has a value close to 1, like* r $= 0.8$ *or* 0.9, *we have high positive correlation.* r $= -0.8$ *or* -0.9 *is said to be high negative correlation.* For these values of r, two corresponding standard scores will be close to each other in value.

Values of r *close to zero indicate low correlation.*

For $r = 0$, the regression equations become

$$y = 0\frac{\sigma_y}{\sigma_x}x$$

or

$$y = 0 \text{ or the } X \text{ axis}$$

and

$$x = 0\frac{\sigma_x}{\sigma_y}y$$

or

$$x = 0 \text{ or the } Y \text{ axis}$$

No matter what the X score, the first regression equation predicts $y = 0$, and hence the Y score is equal to M_y. Similarly, corresponding to each Y score the second equation will predict M_x. The regression equations are thus of little aid in predicting scores—a lack of any sort of correspondence between pairs of scores is indicated. This is the meaning of zero correlation.

Ex. 20. Describe the position of the regression lines for perfect positive correlation, assuming that $\sigma_y = \sigma_x$, that is, that the characters being measured are equally variable.

Ex. 21. Describe the position of the regression lines for perfect negative correlation, if the characters being measured are equally variable.

Reliability of the Correlation Coefficient. A correlation coefficient, like the other measures with which we have worked, is subject to sampling errors. Suppose that the correlation between I.Q. and school achievement is found to be 0.70 for a sample of 200 children. The actual correlation may be higher or lower. The formula for the standard error of a correlation coefficient is

$$\sigma_r = \frac{1 - r^2}{\sqrt{N}}$$

Thus if $r = 0.70$ for a sample of 200 cases

$$\sigma_r = \frac{1 - 0.49}{\sqrt{200}} = \frac{0.51}{10\sqrt{2}} = \frac{0.051\sqrt{2}}{2} = 0.035$$

$$\text{P.E.}_r = \frac{2}{3}(0.035) = 0.023$$

Then it is customary to write $r = 0.70 + 0.02$, approximately, and the true r is almost sure to lie between

$$0.70 - 3(0.035)$$

and

$$0.70 + 3(0.035)$$

or between 0.60 and 0.81, approximately.

Errors of Estimate. We have used the regression equations to estimate the *most probable* value of a Y score when an X score was given, or the most probable value of an X score when a Y score was given. These estimates are naturally subject to error, since they assume that all points fall exactly on the regression lines. The following formulas measure the degree of that error.

The standard error of an estimated Y score is:

$$\sigma_{(\text{est. } Y)} = \sigma_y \sqrt{1 - r^2}$$

and the standard error of an estimated X score is:

$$\sigma_{(\text{est. } X)} = \sigma_x \sqrt{1 - r^2}$$

The actual Y score will lie between the limits

$$Y \text{ score} \pm 3\,\sigma_{(\text{est. } Y)}$$

and the actual X score will lie between the limits

$$X \text{ score} \pm 3 \ \sigma_{(\text{est. } x)}$$

Suppose $\quad r = 0.7 \qquad N = 200$

$$M_x = 70 \qquad \sigma_x = 7$$
$$M_y = 73 \qquad \sigma_y = 8$$

and we wish to estimate the Y score of a student whose X score is 80.

We use the regression equation

$$y = r\frac{\sigma_y}{\sigma_x}x$$
$$x = 80 - 70 = 10$$
$$y = 0.7\frac{8}{7}(10)$$
$$y = 8$$
$$Y \text{ score} = 73 + 8 = 81$$
$$\sigma_{(\text{est. } Y)} = \sigma_y \sqrt{1 - r^2}$$
$$\sigma_{(\text{est. } Y)} = 8 \ \sqrt{1 - 0.49}$$
$$= 8 \ \sqrt{0.51}$$
$$= 8(0.71) = 5.7$$

The actual Y score is almost sure to lie between $81 - 3 \ (5.7)$ and $81 + 3 \ (5.7)$, or between 64 and 98, approximately.

$$\text{P.E.}_{(\text{est. } Y)} = \frac{2}{3} \times 5.7, \text{ approximately}$$
$$= 3.8$$

and the customary way of writing the estimated Y score would be 81 ± 3.8.

If we are to estimate the X score of a student whose Y score is 65, we have

$$x = r\frac{\sigma_x}{\sigma_y}y$$
$$x = 0.7\frac{7}{8}(-8)$$
$$x = -4.9$$

The X score $= 70 - 4.9 = 65.1.$

$$\sigma_{(\text{est. } X)} = 7\sqrt{1 - 0.49}$$
$$= 7\,(0.71) = 4.97 = 5.0 \text{ approximately}$$

The actual Y score is almost sure to lie between $65.1 - 3$ (5) and $65.1 + 3$ (5) or between 50 and 80 approximately, and P.E.$_{(\text{est. } X)} = \dfrac{2}{3}\,(4.97) = 3.3$, approximately, and we would write:

Estimated X score $= 65.1 \pm 3.3.$

Ex. 22. Find the standard errors of the correlation coefficient and of the estimates in Ex. 14. Between what limits does the true correlation coefficient probably lie? Give limits for the estimates also. $N = 100.$

Ex. 23. Answer the same question as in the previous example, using the data of Ex. 15.

Let us illustrate here that a correlation coefficient derived from a small number of cases is not very reliable.

Suppose that we have as few as 16 cases and that $r = 0.80.$

$$\sigma_r = \frac{1 - 0.64}{\sqrt{16}} = \frac{0.36}{4} = 0.09$$

Then the true value of r is almost sure to lie between the limits 0.80 ± 0.27, that is, between 0.53 and 1.07. Hence although the result 0.80 would indicate a fairly high correlation, the true correlation may be as low as 0.53. On the other hand, perfect correlation may exist.

Suppose that we have only 16 cases and find the correlation to be 0.30.

$$\sigma_r = \frac{1 - 0.09}{4} = \frac{0.91}{4} = 0.23$$

Then the extreme limits for r are 0.30 ± 0.69, that is, -0.39 and $+0.99$. Thus correlation may be *low negative* or else *high positive*.

Thus we see that a correlation study, in order to be reliable, should be made from a fairly large sample. It should not include fewer than 25 cases.

Ex. 24. On the basis of Table 58, answer the following:

(1) In which subjects were students best able to predict their marks? least able? How might this be explained?

(2) Would you say that, in general, these students are fairly good at predicting their grades?

(3) Which is the least reliable correlation coefficient? How might this be explained?

(4) Between what two limits does the true correlation coefficient for library service lie? for physics?

(5) On the basis of these results, would you say that college students in general (that is, the whole group, of which this group is a sample) are fairly good at predicting their grades? Explain.

TABLE 58*

RELATION BETWEEN PREDICTED GRADES AND ASSIGNED GRADES, EXPRESSED IN TERMS OF COEFFICIENTS OF CORRELATION, FOR THE VARIOUS DEPARTMENTS OF INSTRUCTION

Department of instruction	Coefficient of correlation	P.E.$_r$
Agriculture	0.67	0.028
Art	.51	.032
Biology	.70	.030
Chemistry	.84	.024
Commerce and economics	.73	.024
Education	.65	.016
English	.59	.019
Foreign language	.74	.086
Geography and geology	.70	.027
Government	.69	.044
Health and physical education	.68	.029
History	.71	.016
Home economics	.60	.110
Industrial arts	.25	.040
Library science	.47	.074
Mathematics	.66	.020
Music	.47	.041
Physics	.86	.029
All departments	0.65	0.007

* From "The Ability of College Students to Predict Their Grades" by H. L. Donovan and William C. Jones, *Peabody Journal of Education*, July, 1933.

TABLE 59a†

CORRELATIONS WITH INTELLIGENCE

Test or scale	r	P.E.$_r$
Emotional attitude	0.142	0.047
Health knowledge	.425	.039
Good citizenship	.282	.044
War-peace attitude	.053	.047
Scholastic average	.412	.040
Behavior rating (A)	.257	.045
Behavior rating (B)	.238	.045

TABLE 59b†

CORRELATIONS WITH SCHOLASTIC AVERAGE

Test or scale	r	P.E.$_r$
Good citizenship	0.141	0.047
Behavior rating (A)	.566	.032
Behavior rating (B)	.458	.039
Intelligence	.412	.040

† From "An Evaluation of Certain Aspects of a Program of Character Education," by D. D. Feder and L. W. Miller, *Journal of Educational Psychology*, May, 1933.

Ex. 25. On the basis of Tables 59:

(1) Does intelligence seem to be related to any of the other qualities listed? Explain.

(2) From the data would you conclude that the more intelligent children would be likely to behave better than the less intelligent? Would the children who do well in their studies also behave well?

(3) Does intelligence seem to make for good citizenship? Does scholarship seem to influence citizenship?

(4) Discuss the reliability of the correlation coefficients listed.

Correlation in a Two-Way Frequency Table. Again, as in the case of other measures, the computation of a correlation coefficient for a large number of cases would involve an enormous amount of arithmetic. Hence, approximate methods are used once more in order to shorten this work.

In Table 60 we have listed the Army Alpha and Achievement scores of a group of sophomores specializing in mathematics and science at the New Jersey State Teachers College at Montclair. Now, it is evident that we have material here for two frequency tables. In order to group these data, then, we use a *two-way frequency table*. The scores have been tallied and arranged in a two-way table in Table 61. The same rules for grouping data listed for a single distribution in Chapter I also apply here.

TABLE 60

ARMY ALPHA AND ACHIEVEMENT SCORES OF MATHEMATICS AND SCIENCE STUDENTS AT THE NEW JERSEY STATE TEACHERS COLLEGE AT MONTCLAIR

Army Alpha	Achievement	A. A.	Ach.	A. A.	Ach.	A. A.	Ach.	A. A.	Ach.
195	53	184	36	177	41	172	50	161	38
194	51	182	43	177	42	170	45	157	45
192	40	182	50	176	43	169	37	156	45
189	42	180	34	175	51	164	51	153	39
189	41	179	36	175	52	162	32	153	40
189	47	179	38	175	32	162	40	127	46
				173	44				

TABLE 61

ARMY ALPHA SCORES (X)

ACHIEVEMENT SCORES (Y)	125.5–135.5	135.5–145.5	145.5–155.5	155.5–165.5	165.5–175.5	175.5–185.5	185.5–195.5	F_y
50.5–55.5				/	//		//	5
45.5–50.5	/				/	/	//	5
40.5–45.5				//	//	////	/	9
35.5–40.5			//	//	/	///	/	9
30.5–35.5				/	/	/		3
F_x	1	0	2	6	7	9	6	$N = 31$

Ex. 26. Group the data in Table 20 into a two-way frequency table.
Ex. 27. Group the data in Table 62 into a two-way frequency table.

Approximate Graphic Treatment of Correlation in a Two-Way Frequency Table.

We shall presently see how to make an exact mathematical study of linear correlation from a two-way table by computing the correlation coefficient and obtaining the regression equations.

TABLE 62

ARMY ALPHA AND ACHIEVEMENT SCORES OF 103 SOPHOMORES OF THE NEW JERSEY STATE TEACHERS COLLEGE AT MONTCLAIR

Army Alpha	Achievement	A. A.	Ach.	A. A.	Ach.	A. A.	Ach.
209	54	182	50	175	52	164	42
199	41	182	43	175	51	162	40
198	37	181	46	175	32	162	40
197	45	181	42	174	56	162	32
195	53	180	53	174	44	161	50
195	53	180	53	173	44	161	46
194	51	180	50	172	50	161	38
194	43	180	48	172	45	160	38
192	40	180	47	171	42	158	51
191	54	180	47	171	42	157	45
189	47	180	34	170	45	157	44
189	42	179	59	170	42	156	45
189	41	179	46	169	44	156	45
187	51	179	38	169	39	156	40
187	51	179	38	169	37	155	41
187	50	179	36	168	43	153	40
186	60	178	46	168	41	153	39
186	48	178	43	168	40	153	36
186	43	177	43	168	38	151	49
184	54	177	42	167	49	148	35
184	50	177	41	167	45	147	41
184	36	177	38	166	45	145	43
184	36	176	50	166	38	144	51
183	49	176	43	165	32	144	45
183	48	176	31	164	51	141	50
183	36					135	48
						127	46

In general, this process involves considerable computation. Hence we shall now outline a crude graphic procedure, which, however, is adequate for any or all of the following purposes:

1. To indicate whether approximate *linear* correlation exists.
2. If approximate linear correlation exists, to give some idea of the position of the regression lines.
3. If linear correlation does not exist, to indicate whether curvilinear correlation does, or whether there seems to be no relationship of any sort.

TABLE 63

REGULAR-TIME AND NO-TIME-LIMIT RAW SCORES IN THE OHIO STATE UNIVERSITY PSYCHOLOGICAL TEST*

SCORES — REGULAR TIME

SCORES–NO. TIME LIMIT	34.5–54.5	54.5–74.5	74.5–94.5	94.5–114.5	114.5–134.5	134.5–154.5	154.5–174.5	174.5–194.5	194.5–214.5	F_y
264.5–274.5							×1			1
254.5–264.5				1	2	1	3x	3	1	11
244.5–254.5				1		6 x	2	2	2	13
234.5–244.5				3	2	x 4	2			11
224.5–234.5		1	1	6	x 6	3				17
214.5–224.5	1•		4	6	x 6	2				19
204.5–214.5		1	1	7	x 4	2				15
194.5–204.5			1	2 x	2					5
184.5–194.5		1	4 x	2		1				8
174.5–184.5			3 x	1						4
164.5–174.5		2	x 3	1						6
154.5–164.5		1	1 x	1						3
144.5–154.5		2 x		1						3
134.5–144.5		1 x								1
F_x	1	9	18	31	23	19	8	5	3	117

From "The Factor of Speed," by Frank S. Freeman, Journal of General Psychology, April 1932.

The method is based on the fact that, if linear correlation exists, the position of the regression line $y = r\frac{\sigma_y}{\sigma_x}x$ will be well indicated by plotting the points whose abscissas are the actual X scores for a particular column, and ordinates the median of the Y scores in that column. (If curvilinear correlation exists, some indication as to the position of the trend curve will be indicated by these points.)

These points can be plotted directly in the table. In Table 63 we have carried out this process. The median of the first column is naturally the single score found there. We have placed a dot at this point. In the second column, we have counted up $4\frac{1}{2}$, and placed a dot at this point. In the third column we have

TABLE 64

HYPOTHETICAL ILLUSTRATION OF LOW CORRELATION

X SCORE

Y SCORE	35	40	45	50	55	60	65	70	75	80	85	F_y
85	2		1		2	1	1	×3	5		1	16
80	1		2		3	1	4×	1	4	2	2	20
75	1	1			1		1 ×	1	3			8
70						2		×			2	4
65		3			4×		1		1	1		10
60		2	4●	5×		2		2	1		1	17
55					3		× ●		1	1	●1	6
50		1	3	3				×4		1	3	15
45				2				2	×	●4		8
40				1		1	1	1	1	×3	3	11
F_x	4	7	10	11	10	8	10	14	16	12	13	115

TABLE 65

HYPOTHETICAL ILLUSTRATION OF CURVILINEAR CORRELATION

X SCORE

Y SCORE	25	30	35	40	45	50	55	60	65	70	F_y
75										1	1
70									1	1	2
65		1							4		5
60	2	2						3	4		11
55	4●				1	2	2				9
50	2		2	1		1	4	3●			13
45		4	3	3	3	2	4	3			22
40			6	2	4	5					17
35				4	4						8
F_x	8	7	11	10	12	10	10	9	9	2	88

counted up 9, in the fourth $15\frac{1}{2}$, etc. We have sketched in an approximation to the position of the regression line.

In the same way the position of the regression line $x = r\dfrac{\sigma_x}{\sigma_y}y$ will be indicated by the points whose ordinates are actual y scores and whose abscissas are the medians of the rows. We have used crosses to indicate these points. In the second row, for example, we have counted $5\frac{1}{2}$ to the right, in the third $6\frac{1}{2}$, etc. We have a linear trend indicated once more, and have drawn in an approximation to the second regression line.

We have applied the same method to the hypothetical data of Table 64 to indicate the existence of no relationship.

We have applied this method to the hypothetical data of Table 65 to indicate the existence of curvilinear correlation.

Ex. 28. Make a graphic study of correlation in Tables 61, 67, 68. If linear correlation is indicated, make an approximate sketch of the regression lines. If curvilinear correlation is indicated, make an approximate sketch of the trend curves.

Mathematical Treatment of Correlation in a Two-Way Frequency Table. The formula[1] for r which we shall now apply is

$$r = \frac{\dfrac{\Sigma\xi\eta}{N} - c_x c_y}{\sigma_x\sigma_y}$$

where ξ and η are deviations from the *estimated mean* of the X scores and the *estimated mean* of the Y scores, respectively; c_x is the correction for the estimated mean of the X scores; c_y is the correction for the estimated mean of the Y scores; σ_x and σ_y are the standard deviations of the X and Y scores respectively.

In Table 66 we have found r for the data of Table 61. We have also found M_x, M_y, the regression equations, and the standard errors, since the use of the regression equations for predictive purposes would require all these facts.

The work for finding c_x, c_y, σ_x, σ_y is merely a repetition of the processes with which we became familiar in Chapters II and III. Finding $\Sigma\xi\eta$ is a new matter. Note that a line has been drawn

[1] A derivation of this formula will be found in Note V of the Appendix.

ACHIEVEMENT SCORES (Y) × ARMY ALPHA SCORES (X)

ACHIEVEMENT SCORES (Y)	ARMY ALPHA SCORES (X) 125.5–135.5	135.5–145.5	145.5–155.5	155.5–165.5	165.5–175.5	175.5–185.5	185.5–195.5	F_y	η_y	$F_y\eta_y$	$F_y\eta_y^2$	$\Sigma\xi\eta$
50.5–55.5	-4 1 -4			-2 1 -2	0 2 0		8 2 4	5	2	10	20	6
45.5–50.5			4 2 2	0 1 0	0 1 0	1 1 1	4 2 2	5	1	5	5	1
40.5–45.5				0 2 0	0 2 0	0 4 0	0 1 0	9	0	0	0	0
35.5–40.5			2 2 -2	0 0 0	0 1 -1	-3 3 -3	-2 1 -2	9	-1	-9	9	1
30.5–35.5				2 1 2	0 1 0	-2 1 -2	-2 1 -2	3	-2	-6	12	0
F_x	1	0	2	6	7	9	6	N=31		0	46	8
ξ_x	-4	-3	-2	-1	0	1	2					
$F_x\xi_x$	-4	0	-4	-6	0	9	12	7				
$F_x\xi_x^2$	16	0	8	6	0	9	24	63				

TABLE 66

through the row containing the estimated mean of the Y's and another line has been drawn through the column containing the estimated mean of the X's. Now let us examine the entries in the top row. The first one is a 1. The deviation of this score from the estimated mean of the X's is -1 class-interval (it is one column to the *left* of the one marked), and its deviation from the estimated mean of the Y scores is 2 class-intervals (it is 2 rows *above* the one marked). Then $\xi\eta$ for this score is $-1 \times 2 = -2$. This number has been entered in the lower left-hand corner of the cell.

The next entry in this row is a 2. Since this 2 lies in the marked column, $\xi = 0$. Since it is 2 rows above the marked row, $\eta = 2$. Hence $\xi\eta = 0 \times 2 = 0$, and the entry in the lower left-hand corner is a zero.

The last cell of the top row also contains an entry. We place $2 \times 2 = 4$ in the lower left-hand corner of this cell, since it is 2 columns to the right and 2 rows above the marked column and row respectively, and hence $\xi = 2$ class-intervals, $\eta = 2$ class-intervals.

The entries in the lower left-hand corners in second-row cells are $-4 \times 1 = -4, 0 \times 1 = 0, 1 \times 1 = 1, 2 \times 1 = 2$ respectively. Similar entries have been made in the other rows.

Now, let us explain the entries in the upper right-hand corners of the cells. For the last cell in the top row, we have just found that $\xi\eta = 4$. Since $\xi\eta = 4$ for each score, and there are 2 scores, we have a total of 8 for this cell. This number has been placed in the upper right-hand corner of the cell.

In the fourth row, we have a cell containing 3. For each score in this cell, $\xi\eta = (1)(-1) = -1$. For all 3, we have -3. Hence -1 and -3 fill the left- and right-hand corners of this cell, respectively.

Thus we see that every entry in the upper right-hand corner of a cell is obtained by multiplying the entry in the lower left-hand corner by the number in the cell.

Note that the entries for the row and column of estimated means are all zeroes. For every entry in the marked column $\xi = 0$. Hence for all such entries $\xi\eta = 0$.

The upper right-hand corner entries have been summed for each row and placed in the $\Sigma \xi \eta$ column, which has then been totaled.

Now $c_x = \dfrac{\Sigma F_x \xi}{N}$, and $c_y = \dfrac{\Sigma F_y \eta}{N}$.

$$\sigma_x = \left[\sqrt{\dfrac{\Sigma F_x \xi^2}{N} - c_x^2} \right] \times i_x, \text{ and } \sigma_y = \left[\sqrt{\dfrac{\Sigma F_y \eta^2}{N} - c_y^2} \right] \times i_y$$

where F_x and F_y are frequencies of X and Y scores, respectively.

i_x and i_y are class-intervals of X and Y scores, respectively.

$c_x = \dfrac{7}{31} = 0.3$ class-interval $c_y = \dfrac{0}{31} = 0$ class-intervals

$= (0.3)(10) = 3$ units $= 0$ units

$\sigma_x = \sqrt{\dfrac{63}{31} - (0.3)^2}$ $\sigma_y = \sqrt{\dfrac{46}{31} - (0)^2}$

$= 1.4$ class-intervals $= 1.2$ class-intervals

$= 1.4 \times 10 = 14$ $= 1.2 \times 5 = 6.0$

$$r = \dfrac{\dfrac{8}{31} - (0.3)(0)}{(1.4)(1.2)} = \dfrac{0.26 - 0}{1.68} = 0.15 = 0.2, \text{ approximately}$$

Estimated mean of the X's $= 170.5$

$+ c_x = 3$

$\overline{}$

$M_x = 173.5$

Estimated mean of the Y's $= 43$

$+ c_y = 0$

$\overline{}$

$M_y = 43$

Regression equations:

$y = 0.2\dfrac{6}{14}x$ $y = 0.09x$

$x = 0.2\dfrac{14}{6}y$ $x = 0.5y$

Standard errors:

$\sigma_r = \dfrac{1 - 0.04}{\sqrt{31}} = 0.17$

$\sigma_{(\text{est. } X)} = 14 \sqrt{1 - 0.04} = 13.7$

$\sigma_{(\text{est. } Y)} = 6 \sqrt{1 - 0.04} = 5.9$

(For purposes of illustration we have worked out the regression equations. It is evident that they would be of little value for predictive purposes since both the correlation coefficient and the estimate made from the regression equations would be very unreliable.)

All results are in class-intervals, and in the case of X measures are multiplied by 10 to obtain ordinary units, since the class-interval of the X's is 10. Similarly Y measures are multiplied by the Y class-interval of 5.

In the case of r, all measures have been left in class-intervals to save computation. If they were expressed in ordinary units, the result would be the same. Let us demonstrate this fact.

Since ξ must be multiplied by 10 and η by 5 in order to change to ordinary units, $\xi\eta$ must be multiplied by 50.

Thus, in ordinary units:

$$r = \frac{\dfrac{8}{31}(50) - (0.3)(10)(0)(5)}{(1.4)(10)(1.2)(5)}$$

and dividing numerator and denominator by 50, we have:

$$r = \frac{\dfrac{8}{31} - (0.3)(0)}{(1.4)(1.2)}$$

which is the value we have used.

Ex. 29. Find r from the table which you have made for the data of Table 20.

Ex. 30. Find r from the data in Table 65.

Ex. 31. Find r from the two-way table which you have made for the data of Table 62. Find M_x, M_y, the regression equations, and standard errors.

Ex. 32. Find r, M_x, M_y, the regression equations, and the standard errors for the data in Tables 63, 64, 67.

TABLE 67

RELATION BETWEEN MILLER MENTAL ABILITY TEST AVERAGES FORMS A AND B, AND OBJECTIVE TEST*

Average in Miller A and B	22.5–27.5	27.5–32.5	32.5–37.5	37.5–42.5	42.5–47.5	47.5–52.5	52.5–57.5	57.5–62.5	62.5–67.5	67.5–72.5	72.5–77.5	77.5–82.5	F_y
62.5–67.5....						2	3	2				1	8
57.5–62.5....			1	1	3	3	5	2	4	2			21
52.5–57.5....			2	4	3	8	7	3	1	1			29
47.5–52.5....		1	2	5	7	8	5	2					30
42.5–47.5....	2	1	2	3	2	6		1	4				21
37.5–42.5....			1		2	2	3						8
32.5–37.5....	1	1		2	3	3		1					11
27.5–32.5....			1	1	2		1						5
22.5–27.5....		1						1					2
17.5–22.5....			2		1								3
12.5–17.5....													0
7.5–12.5....													0
2.5– 7.5....					1								1
F_x..........	3	4	11	16	24	32	24	12	9	3	0	1	139

* From "An Objective Test in Educational Psychology" by W. S. Miller, *Journal of Educational Psychology*, April, 1925.

Ex. 33. Find the correlation between achievement in history and achievement in English, using the data in Table 68.

TABLE 68

GRADES IN ENTRANCE EXAMINATIONS IN HISTORY AND ENGLISH MADE BY 479 APPLICANTS FOR ADMISSION TO THE NEW JERSEY STATE TEACHERS COLLEGE AT MONTCLAIR

HISTORY (Y)	ENGLISH (X)									F_y
	55.5–60.5	60.5–65.5	65.5–70.5	70.5–75.5	75.5–80.5	80.5–85.5	85.5–90.5	90.5–95.5	95.5–100.5	
95.5–100.5....	1	3	10	22	29	66	53	36	2	222
90.5– 95.5....	2	2	4	13	18	19	27	11	1	97
85.5– 90.5....	0	0	2	6	14	8	17	7	2	56
80.5– 85.5....	0	0	1	8	4	9	9	5	1	37
75.5– 80.5....	0	1	1	7	7	8	6	4	1	35
70.5– 75.5....	0	0	0	2	3	2	3	1	0	11
65.5– 70.5....	0	0	0	1	3	1	1	0	1	7
60.5– 65.5....	0	0	0	0	2	2	1	0	0	5
55.5– 60.5....	0	0	1	2	0	1	0	0	0	4
50.5– 55.5....	0	0	0	0	0	1	2	1	0	4
45.5– 50.5....	0	1	0	0	0	0	0	0	0	1
F_x	3	7	19	61	80	117	119	65	8	$N = 479$

Rank-Difference Formula. The formula for the correlation coefficient and the method of computing it which we have just used are well suited to data expressed in *numerical* form for a *large number* of cases. Sometimes differences in value are expressed in *rank* rather than numerical form. Thus, numerical ratings for cooperation, industry, honesty, courtesy, efficiency, neatness, etc., might be difficult to assign. In measuring capacities of this type, ratings in rank form are often employed. Again, when the number of cases is small (fewer than 25), the coefficient of correlation is not reliable, and hence merely indicates the possibility of some relation between the quantities measured. Hence it is not worth while, in such a case, to perform laborious computations, and the use of a formula involving less work is advisable. The rank-difference formula, whose use we shall now explain, is used in the two cases just discussed.

To rank a set of numerical scores, the highest score is ranked 1, the next highest 2, the next 3, etc. For example, we have:

Score	Rank
85	3
65	7
73	6
80	4
40	9
95	1
77	5
62	8
25	10
92	2

Sometimes the same score occurs several times. For example:

Score	Rank
90	2
75	3.5
75	3.5
60	5
95	1

In this illustration, 95 is the highest score, and hence its rank is 1; 90 has a rank of 2. The next highest score, 75, occurs twice.

The next two ranks would be 3 and 4. It is customary to assign the *median*, 3.5, of these two ranks as the rank of the two scores of 75.

In the example:

Score	Preliminary rank	Rank
60........................	(9)	10.5
75........................	(5)	6
80........................	3	3
60........................	(10)	10.5
75........................	(6)	6
75........................	(7)	6
90........................	2	2
80........................	4	4
60........................	(11)	10.5
95........................	1	1
65........................	8	8
60........................	(12)	10.5

there are three scores of 75, to which preliminary ranks of 5, 6, and 7 are given. For the final ranks, the *median* rank 6 is chosen. There are four scores of 60 to which the preliminary ranks 9, 10, 11, 12 are given. The median of this set is 10.5, and this is chosen for the final ranks.

Ex. 34. Rank the scores 40, 65, 90, 75, 72, 85, 65, 75, 77, 87, 75, 65, 97, 65, 75, 48, 80, 80, 91, 63.

When data are in rank form, a rough measure of the correlation is given by Spearman's formula

$$\rho = 1 - \frac{6\Sigma D^2}{N(N^2 - 1)}$$

where ρ is the Greek letter rho, and D represents the difference in ranks.

The method of calculating ρ is illustrated in Table 69, where it measures the correlation between disciplinary value and interest for various school subjects.

TABLE 69*

	Rank for disciplinary value	Rank for interest	D	D²
English literature..........	3	4	−1	1
English composition........	8	6	2	4
History...................	2	2	0	0
Algebra..................	10	10	0	0
Geometry................	11	11	0	0
Latin....................	7	9	−2	4
Science..................	1	1	0	0
Athletics.................	4	3	1	1
Unskilled labor...........	9	8	1	1
Skilled labor.............	5	7	−2	4
Teaching................	6	5	1	1

$$\Sigma D^2 = 16$$

* Data from E. L. Thorndike, "The Disciplinary Values of Studies in the Opinion of Students," *Teachers College Record*, v. 25, 1924, p. 142.

$$\rho = 1 - \frac{6\Sigma D^2}{N(N^2 - 1)} = 1 - \frac{96}{11(121 - 1)} = 1 - 0.07 = 0.93$$
$$r = 0.9359 = 0.94, \text{ approximately}$$

Pearson has given a corrective formula for converting ρ into r. Table 71 has been worked out by the use of this formula, and we have used it to obtain r. For $\rho = 0.93$, the table indicates $r = 0.94$.

Ex. 35. Find ρ and then r for the data of Table 70, that is, the correlation between faculty opinion and student opinion on qualities of good citizenship.

Ex. 36. Express the data of Table 20 in rank form and then find ρ and r.

Ex. 37. Express the data of Table 51 in rank form and then find ρ and r.

TABLE 70*

Most Frequently Mentioned Qualities of Good Citizenship as Ranked by Faculty and Pupils

Quality	Rank by faculty	Rank by pupils
Cooperation	1	1
Honesty	2	4.5
Active participation in school activities	3	8
Responsibility	4.5	7
Consideration of others and their views	4.5	15.5
Sincerity	6.5	13
Courtesy	6.5	10.5
Industry	8	4.5
Scholarship	9	13
High ideals of duty	11	13
Seriousness of purpose	11	15.5
Loyalty to school	11	2.5
Wholesome attitude toward work	13	20.5
Ability to gain good will of others	14	9
Reaction to criticism	15	18.5
Initiative and originality	17	10.5
Courage to defend one's self	17	22
Common sense	17	20.5
Leadership	19	2.5
Character	20	17
Modesty	21	18.5
Energy	22	6
Popularity	23	23.5
Offices held	24	23.5

* Data (with slight modification to suit computational purposes) from William C. Reavis, "Method of Selecting the Members of the High School Honor Society," *School Review*, June, 1928.

Ex. 38. Bring in material from educational periodicals to illustrate the use of correlation.

TABLE 71

ρ	r	ρ	r	ρ	r	ρ	r
0.01	0.0105	0.26	0.2714	0.51	0.5277	0.76	0.7750
.02	.0209	.27	.2818	.52	.5378	.77	.7847
.03	.0314	.28	.2922	.53	.5479	.78	.7943
.04	.0419	.29	.3025	.54	.5580	.79	.8039
.05	.0524	.30	.3129	.55	.5680	.80	.8135
.06	.0628	.31	.3232	.56	.5781	.81	.8230
.07	.0733	.32	.3335	.57	.5881	.82	.8325
.08	.0838	.33	.3439	.58	.5981	.83	.8421
.09	.0942	.34	.3542	.59	.6081	.84	.8516
.10	.1047	.35	.3645	.60	.6181	.85	.8610
.11	.1151	.36	.3748	.61	.6280	.86	.8705
.12	.1256	.37	.3850	.62	.6379	.87	.8799
.13	.1360	.38	.3935	.63	.6478	.88	.8893
.14	.1465	.39	.4056	.64	.6577	.89	.8986
.15	.1569	.40	.4158	.65	.6676	.90	.9080
.16	.1674	.41	.4261	.66	.6775	.91	.9173
.17	.1778	.42	.4363	.67	.6873	.92	.9269
.18	.1882	.43	.4465	.68	.6971	.93	.9359
.19	.1986	.44	.4567	.69	.7069	.94	.9451
.20	.2091	.45	.4669	.70	.7167	.95	.9543
.21	.2195	.46	.4771	.71	.7265	.96	.9635
.22	.2299	.47	.4872	.72	.7363	.97	.9727
.23	.2403	.48	.4973	.73	.7460	.98	.9818
.24	.2507	.49	.5075	.74	.7557	.99	.9909
.25	.2611	.50	.5176	.75	.7654	1.00	1.0000

Summary. In this chapter we have dealt with the meaning of *linear correlation*. To define this term mathematically, we introduced some elementary theory of *curve-fitting* and arrived at the meaning of a *correlation coefficient*. We have used the following formulas:

$$Correlation\ coefficient:\quad r = \frac{\Sigma xy}{\sqrt{\Sigma x^2 \Sigma y^2}}$$

where x and y represent deviations from the means of the two sets of scores respectively.

Regression lines:
$$y = \frac{r\sigma_y}{\sigma_x}x$$

$$x = \frac{r\sigma_x}{\sigma_y}y$$

Standard errors:
$$\sigma_r = \frac{1 - r^2}{\sqrt{N}}$$

$$\sigma_{(\text{est. } X)} = \sigma_x\sqrt{1 - r^2}$$

$$\sigma_{(\text{est. } Y)} = \sigma_y\sqrt{1 - r^2}$$

Correlation coefficient:
$$r = \frac{\dfrac{\Sigma\xi\eta}{N} - c_x c_y}{\sigma_x \sigma_y}$$

where x and y represent deviations from *estimated* means.

CHAPTER VIII

FURTHER APPLICATIONS OF CORRELATION

Applications of Correlation to Testing. One of the important applications of educational statistics in general, and of correlation in particular, is furnished by the preparation and evaluation of standardized tests. In this connection, we shall study what is meant by the terms *reliability* and *validity*.

Reliability. The *reliability* of a test is defined as the *consistency* with which it measures some particular capacity of those taking it.

One method of estimating this consistency is to study the results obtained by the students in duplicate forms of the same test given at different times. If the students who rate high in the first form, rate high, in general, in the second form, and similarly, if those who rate low in the first form rate low in the second form, evidently the two forms consistently measure the same thing. If, on the other hand, there are large differences in the results obtained by most of the students, evidently the forms do not consistently measure the same capacity.

Now we have seen that the *correlation* between the scores obtained on the two forms will furnish a numerical measure of such consistency. Hence the correlation between scores obtained by the same students in two forms of the same test is called the *reliability coefficient* of that test. The higher the correlation coefficient thus obtained, the greater the reliability of the test.

No definite lower bound can be set for the reliability of tests in general, but in intelligence tests, for example, a reliability of 0.8 or 0.9 is expected.

If duplicate forms of a test are not available, the same test is given to the same group after an interval of time, and again the correlation between scores, or *self-correlation*, is used as the *reliability coefficient*. This is a less desirable procedure, since scores in the repeated test tend to be influenced by the practice effect, by lack of interest on the part of students, by their tendency to repeat errors previously made, etc.

Ex. 1. The data in Table 72 are taken from "A Study of Standard Tests and Teacher-Made Objective Tests in Foods" by Fay V. Perry and M. E. Brown in the *Journal of Educational Research*, October, 1932. One of the purposes of this study was to determine whether teacher-made tests in foods are as reliable as standard tests. Tests *A*, *B*, *C*, and *X* were teacher-made tests, and the others were standardized tests.

A and *B* were duplicate forms of the same test, and the reliability coefficient for this test was determined by administering the duplicate forms to 116 students in San Diego high schools. The other reliability coefficients were determined by giving the same test twice.

(*a*) In the case of each test, do you think the magnitude of the reliability warrants the general use of the test?

(*b*) From the results of this study, which tests seem the more reliable—the standardized or teacher-made?

(*c*) Since each reliability coefficient is subject to a sampling error, find the limits between which the true reliabilities may lie.

TABLE 72

RELIABILITY COEFFICIENTS OF THE SEVERAL
EXAMINATIONS, 116 CASES

	r
King-Clark	0.66
Illinois	.78
Streeter-Trilling	.67
Test X	.79
Test A-B	.86
Test C	.90

Spearman-Brown Prophecy Formula. If the self-correlation of a test is unsatisfactory, it may be lengthened by the addition of similar material until its reliability is greater. To determine by experimental means just how much a test should be lengthened to produce a desired reliability coefficient would require considerable time and trouble. It is customary, instead, to estimate the required length by means of a formula called the Spearman-Brown *prophecy* formula

$$r_x = \frac{Nr}{1 + (N-1)r}$$

where r = the original reliability coefficient.

r_x = the desired reliability coefficient.

N = the number by which the present length of the test should be multiplied.

Suppose, for example, the reliability of a test is 0.6. What will the reliability be when the test has been made three times as long by the addition of similar material?

Using the formula, we have

$$r_x = \frac{3(0.6)}{1 + 2(0.6)} = \frac{1.8}{2.2} = 0.82$$

Thus the reliability coefficient would be increased from 0.6 to 0.82.

Suppose the reliability coefficient of a test is 0.7. How much (approximately) will the test have to be lengthened to produce a reliability coefficient of 0.9? We have

$$0.9 = \frac{0.7N}{1 + 0.7N - 0.7} = \frac{0.7N}{0.7N + 0.3}$$
$$0.63N + 0.27 = 0.7N$$
$$0.27 = 0.07N$$
$$3\frac{6}{7} = N$$

Hence the test should be made approximately *four* times as long in order to produce the desired reliability.

Ex. 2. The reliability of a test is 0.5. If it is lengthened to four times the present size by the addition of similar material, what will the reliability be?

Ex. 3. In a certain test, the reliability coefficient is 0.6. Approximately how much should the test be lengthened to give a reliability of 0.8?

Ex. 4. In Table 73 check the reliabilities for 100 items by applying the Spearman-Brown prophecy formula to the reliabilities for 50 items.

TABLE 73*

Reliability Form A vs. Form B	Reliability 50 items	Reliability 100 items
Type		
Recall..............................	0.811	0.896
5 response..........................	.796	.886
3 response..........................	.598	.748
2 response..........................	.737	.849
True-False.........................	.550	.714

* Data from "Comparative Reliabilities of Five Types of Objective Examinations" by G. M. Ruch and G. D. Stoddard, *Journal of Educational Psychology*, February, 1925.

Ex. 5. Find how many times approximately each of the tests in Table 72 of Ex. 1 should be lengthened to produce a reliability of 0.90.

When a test is increased in length, the Spearman-Brown prophecy formula will work exactly only if the reliability of the questions added is equal to the reliability of the original test, a condition possible theoretically, but difficult to achieve exactly in practice. If theory and practice were in perfect agreement, it would be possible to obtain any degree of reliability by lengthening a test sufficiently.

Practice shows, however, that the Spearman-Brown prophecy formula works well up to a fivefold lengthening of test material, and that, for greater lengthening, reliability does not increase as rapidly as the formula predicts.

Split-Test Method to Determine Reliability. We have seen that the reliability of a test is found by administering duplicate forms of the test, or repeating the original test, if duplicate forms are not available. We have pointed out that the latter procedure does not lead to the best results.

A much better procedure, according to Kelley, is the *split-test method*. This makes use of the *Spearman-Brown formula* as follows: Each student is given two scores by dividing the test items in half by any suitable device which makes the two parts approximately equal in difficulty and content. His scores may be the ratings in the odd and the even items, for example. The correlation between the two sets of scores thus obtained is the *reliability* of the half test. The reliability of the whole test is found by using $N = 2$ in the Spearman-Brown formula. In

Table 74, for example, the "reliability coefficients for each of the six tests were obtained by correlating the first and last five rows of the score table."*

TABLE 74

RELIABILITY COEFFICIENTS FOR THE SEASHORE TESTS*

	This study r	Ruch and Stoddard r	Brown r
Pitch.....................	0.66	0.70	0.71
Intensity...............	.86	.66	.65
Time....................	.81	.53	.48
Consonance.............	.52	.32	.43
Memory.................	.88	.66	.59
Rhythm.................	.64	.50	.29

* From "Measuring Musical Ability and Achievement—A Study of the Correlation of Seashore Test Scores and Other Variables" by James L. Mirsell, *Journal of Educational Research*, February, 1932.

Ex. 6. Comment on the reliability of the various parts of the Seashore test, as indicated by the data of Table 74.

Ex. 7. The reliability coefficients in the first row of Table 75 were obtained by splitting the tests into two forms of 25 questions each. Check the entries in rows 2 and 3 by the use of the Spearman-Brown formula.

TABLE 75

TOOPS'S DATA. COMPARISON OF THE RELIABILITY COEFFICIENT OF THE RECALL, RECOGNITION, TRUE-FALSE TESTS WITH CERTAIN ADDITIONS*

	Recall	5 response	True-False
1. Reliability (of halves) two forms of 25 each	0.448	0.385	0.340
2. Reliability of two 50-question sets (Spearman-Brown $n = 2$).................	.618	.556	.508
3. Reliability of two 100-item sets (Spearman-Brown $n = 4$).................	.764	.715	.673

* Same source as Table 73.

Validity of Test Scores. By the *validity* of a test is meant the degree to which it does measure whatever capacity it purports to measure. The validity of a test is determined by selecting some *criterion*, which is actually known to measure the capacity in question, and finding the correlation between the test and the criterion. For example, the criterion of a mathematics achievement test may be school marks in mathematics.

Table 76 furnishes data on the validity of the Seashore tests as measures of musical capacity. The author of the study from which the data were taken used three criteria—talent ratings of pupils in applied music, piano final grades, and voice final grades. An examination of the correlation coefficients indicates low validity. To quote the author of the article, "Clearly the Seashore Tests show little or no relationship with musical talent as assessed by competent musicians, and if the latter is not a good criterion, where shall we find one?"

TABLE 76

CORRELATION OF TEST SCORES WITH CRITERIA*

	Talent rating	Piano final grade	Voice final grade
	r	r	r
Pitch..................	0.11	0.01	0.07
Intensity.............	.07	.09	.08
Time.................	.20	.10	− .14
Consonance...........	− .27	− .25	.06
Memory..............	.19	.07	.05
Rhythm..............	.25	.20	.06
Average.............	.08	− .15	.08

* Same source as Table 74.

To give another example of the use of a criterion, the authors of the Sangren-Woody Silent Reading Test used as a criterion to measure validity a composite score derived from the following: Stanford Achievement Test, Paragraph Meaning, Sentence Meaning, Word Meaning; Thorndike McCall Reading Scale; Burgess Silent Reading Test; Monroe Reading Test, Rate and Comprehension; teacher's reading marks (average for 3 months). Table 77 gives the correlation between these composite scores and scores on separate parts of the Sangren-Woody Reading Test.

Another method of testing validity is to find correlations between the given test and other, related tests, to reveal what common measuring factors exist. For example, Table 78 gives the various intercorrelations among the different parts of the Seashore test as found by Professor Mirsell. Now, since all parts of this test purport to measure musical capacity, these

TABLE 77*

CORRELATIONS BETWEEN CRITERION SCORES AND
SCORES ON SEPARATE PARTS OF THE SANGREN-
WOODY READING TEST

	r
Criterion and word meaning	0.888
Criterion and rate	.754
Criterion and fact material	.901
Criterion and following directions	.710
Criterion and total meaning	.753
Criterion and central thought	.688
Criterion and organization	.610
Average coefficient	.760
Criterion and total score	.897

* Data from a note, "The Sangren-Woody Silent Reading Test" by Paul V. Sangren, *Journal of Educational Research*, March, 1929.

correlations should be fairly high. Note that they are, however, for the most part, low. To quote the author of the article from which the data are taken: "Brown remarks that the tests evidently measure quite disparate factors, which might show different relationships if combined. And Spearman has shown that the Seashore Tests fail to reveal any common group factor of musical ability, which may indicate either that there is no such factor, or that the tests cannot reveal it, even though it may exist."

TABLE 78*

INTERCORRELATIONS OF SEASHORE TEST SCORES

	Intensity	Time	Consonance	Memory	Rhythm
Pitch	0.30	0.24	0.38	0.49	0.22
Intensity		.51	.28	.21	.32
Time			.085	.29	.23
Consonance				.55	.09
Memory					.38

* Same source as Table 74.

Corrections for a Coefficient of Correlation. We shall now discuss the use of several formulas which have been invented by Spearman to correct errors in the value of a correlation coefficient which may be due to errors in the scores themselves.

Attenuation. "Errors of observation" or "response errors" are inevitable in any series of test scores, for obvious reasons—faulty methods of administering a test, fatigue or unusual emotional stress on the part of students, practice effect, etc. If the number of test items is large, the number of positive errors is likely to be about the same as the number of negative errors. This fact will result in a balancing of errors in the finding of the mean. In the finding of a standard deviation, however, deviations are squared, and the positive results are added; hence all errors tend to make a σ larger.

In the formula for the correlation coefficient, the denominator is $\sigma_x \sigma_y$, and if the σ's are in error by being too large, the correlation coefficient will be in error by being too small. This effect is termed "attenuation" by Spearman.

One method suggested by him to correct this effect is as follows: If the scores in two tests are to be correlated, give each test twice, and find the self-correlation of each test. Then the r corrected for attenuation is given by the formula

$$r_{AB} = \frac{\sqrt{r_{A_1B_2} r_{A_2B_1}}}{\sqrt{r_{A_1A_2} r_{B_1B_2}}}$$

where A and B represent the two tests.

A_1 represents the first set of scores in A.

A_2 represents the second set of scores in A.

B_1 represents the first set of scores in B.

B_2 represents the second set of scores in B.

r_{AB} the corrected correlation between A and B.

$r_{A_1A_2}$ the self-correlation of test A.

$r_{B_1B_2}$ the self-correlation of test B.

$r_{A_1B_2}$ the correlation between the sets A_1 and B_2.

$r_{A_2B_1}$ the correlation between the sets A_2 and B_1.

To illustrate the effect of such a correction, suppose that the "raw" or uncorrected correlations are

$$r_{A_1B_2} = 0.45, \; r_{A_2B_1} = 0.51$$

and the self-correlations are

$$r_{A_1A_2} = 0.81, \; r_{B_1B_2} = 0.75$$

Then the corrected coefficient is

$$r_{AB} = \frac{\sqrt{(0.45)(0.51)}}{\sqrt{(0.81)(0.75)}} = 0.61$$

Thus the correction for attenuation in this case raises the raw r from 0.45 or 0.51 to 0.61.

If only one correlation coefficient between the two given tests is available, the approximate formula

$$r_{AB} = \frac{r_{A_1B_1}}{\sqrt{r_{A_1A_2}r_{B_1B_2}}}$$

is used. (This assumes $r_{A_1B_1} = r_{A_1B_2} = r_{A_2B_1}$.) $r_{A_1A_2}$ and $r_{B_1B_2}$ are *reliability coefficients* which may be obtained by any method (not necessarily by repetition of the tests).

Thus, in the above illustration, if the one correlation coefficient obtained had been 0.45 and the reliability coefficients had been the same

$$r_{AB} = \frac{0.45}{\sqrt{0.81 \times 0.75}} = 0.58$$

This result is not very different from the above.

Ex. 8. Using the second formula for r corrected for attenuation and the reliability coefficients for 100 items in Table 79, check the column for corrected r in Table 79.

TABLE 79*

CORRELATIONS BETWEEN THE RECALL AND FOUR OTHER
TYPES RAW AND CORRECTED FOR ATTENUATION

Type	r (raw)	r (corrected)
5-response	0.767	0.861
3-response	.618	.755
2-response	.622	.713
True-False	.384	.480

* Same source as Table 73.

Correction of a Correlation Coefficient for Heterogeneity.
Kelley has called attention to still another source of error in a
correlation coefficient. He points out that securing a reliability
coefficient of 0.40 from a group composed of children in a single
grade is probably indicative of greater, not less, reliability than
to secure a reliability coefficient of 0.90 from a group composed
of children from all grades. He attributes this result to the
varying range of talent in the two groups. For this reason the
size and variability of a group should always be given in stating
and interpreting reliability coefficients.

Kelley gives a formula to correct for such heterogeneity.
The formula is

$$\frac{\sigma}{\Sigma} = \frac{\sqrt{1-R}}{\sqrt{1-r}}$$

in which σ and Σ are the standard deviations, and r and R are
the reliability coefficients, in the small and large groups, respectively.

Suppose that $r = 0.4$ and $\sigma = 6$ when a test is applied to a
single grade.

To find what R must be in a heterogeneous group to give
evidence of equivalent reliability, if the standard deviation in
this group is 10, we apply the formula and have

$$\frac{6}{10} = \frac{\sqrt{1-R}}{\sqrt{0.6}}$$
$$0.36 = \frac{1-R}{0.6}$$
$$0.216 = 1 - R$$
$$R = 0.78$$

Hence a reliability of 0.4 in the homogeneous group is equivalent to a reliability of 0.78 in the heterogeneous group.

Ex. 9. If $r = 0.5$ and $\sigma = 9$ in a homogeneous group, find the equivalent
reliability in a heterogeneous group whose standard deviation is 15.

Ex. 10. If the reliability of a test is 0.8 in a heterogeneous group whose
standard deviation is 18, find the equivalent reliability in a homogeneous
group whose standard deviation is 8.

Ex. 11. Table 80 is taken from "A Latin Comprehension Test" by B. L. Ullman and T. J. Kirby, *Journal of Educational Research*, November, 1924.

(*a*) Compare the difficulty of Form I and Form II for students in the various semesters. How might this be accounted for?

(*b*) Compare the average results for the various semesters. Explain these.

(*c*) How might you account for the larger reliability coefficients in the higher semesters?

(*d*) Explain the magnitude of the reliability coefficient for all semesters combined.

(*e*) Which indicates the greater reliability—the coefficient of 0.53 for Semester II or the coefficient of 0.85 for all semesters combined? (In other words, correct 0.85 for heterogeneity.)

(*f*) Make the same sort of comparison for Semester IV and all semesters combined; for Semester VI and all semesters combined; for Semester VIII and all semesters combined.

TABLE 80

ULLMAN-KIRBY LATIN COMPREHENSION TEST

	Semester II		Semester IV		Semester VI		Semester VIII		Semesters combined	
	Form I	Form II	Form I	Form II	Form I	Form II	Form I	Form II	Form I	Form II
Pupils tested.....	123	123	101	101	109	109	90	90	423	423
Median..........	11.38	10.15	17.39	18.59	21.81	23.11	25.41	25.67	17.8	19.64
Mean............	11.20	10.17	17.43	18.19	21.58	23.11	24.85	24.67	18.47	18.76
σ.................	2.48	3.96	4.05	3.70	4.79	4.00	4.67	3.99	6.59	6.98
Reliability coefficient...........	0.53 ± 0.04		0.65 ± 0.04		0.57 ± 0.04		0.71 ± 0.04		0.85 ± 0.02	

Curvilinear Correlation. We have seen in the previous chapter that the *correlation coefficient* is a numerical measure of how well the trend of a set of points (each point representing a pair of scores) is described by a *straight line*. We also commented on the fact that correlation is not necessarily linear in nature, that some *curve* other than a straight line may indicate the trend of a set of points.

Correlation Ratio. In order to measure how closely a set of points clusters about any curve, we need a more general measure than the correlation coefficient. Such a measure is furnished by the Pearson *correlation ratio* η (eta).

Since η is a *general* measure of correlation, it may be used even when correlation is linear. In this case, its value is equal to the value of r, the correlation coefficient. By mathematical means, the following facts about η can be demonstrated:

If correlation is curvilinear, η will be numerically greater than r.
If correlation is linear, η = r (numerically).
η is always positive, and may assume any value between 0 and 1.
The value η = 1 indicates perfect correlation.

In the case of linear correlation, there is just one correlation coefficient. In the case of curvilinear correlation, there are two correlation ratios, η_{yx} and η_{xy}, the former giving a measure of the "regression" of y on x, the latter a measure of the regression of x on y. If correlation is linear, $\eta_{yx} = \eta_{xy} = r$.

In linear correlation, when r was computed, it was a simple matter to obtain the two trend or regression lines. In curvilinear correlation, however, obtaining the equations of trend curves is a far more difficult matter. The mathematics involved in finding them would carry us far beyond the scope of this book.

Hence, we shall content ourselves with a study of the formulas for η_{yx} and η_{xy} and the method of computing these ratios.

The formulas are

$$\eta_{yx} = \frac{\sigma_{my}}{\sigma_y}$$

$$\eta_{xy} = \frac{\sigma_{mx}}{\sigma_x}$$

where σ_y and σ_x indicate, as previously, the standard deviations of the Y and X scores respectively, and

$$\sigma_{my} = \sqrt{\frac{\Sigma F_x(\overline{Y}_x - M_y)^2}{N}}$$

where $\overline{Y}_x$ signifies the mean of a Y column and M_y the mean of all the Y scores.

Similarly

$$\sigma_{mx} = \sqrt{\frac{\Sigma F_y(\overline{X}_y - M_x)^2}{N}}$$

where $\overline{X}_y$ signifies the mean of an X row and M_x the mean of all the X scores.

The formula for σ_{my} is recognized to be of the form of a standard deviation. If we refer to Chapter III we find that a standard deviation is of the form:

$$\sigma = \sqrt{\frac{\Sigma F x^2}{N}}$$

where x represents a deviation of a score from the mean.

Now σ_{my} is of this form, the scores being the means of the Y columns, the deviations being taken from M_y.

Table 81 gives the work for calculating η_{yx} from a two-way frequency table. We have used the hypothetical data of Table 65 for this purpose.

Note that the work for finding σ_y and M_y is the same as usual.

In order to find σ_{my}, the mean, $\overline{Y}_x$, of each column, has been found, and entered in the horizontal row marked $\overline{Y}_x$.

Next, M_y has been subtracted from each $\overline{Y}_x$, and the result entered in the row marked $(\overline{Y}_x - M_y)$.

Next, the deviations $(\overline{Y}_x - M_y)$ have been squared.

Finally each $(\overline{Y}_x - M_y)^2$ has been multiplied by the corresponding F_x. The row $F_x(\overline{Y}_x - M_y)^2$ has been added, and divided by the total number of cases in the distribution. σ_{my} and σ_y have been found, and substituted in the formula for η_{yx}.

Table 82 shows the work for computing η_{xy}. It is similar to the work for finding η_{yx}, except that the roles of x and y have been interchanged.

Ex. 12. Find η_{yx} and η_{xy} in Tables 61, 63, 64, 67, 68.

Correction of Correlation Ratio. The correlation ratio should rarely be used unless N, the number of cases in the sample, is large. If N is small, or the number of rows and columns is large, Pearson has given a corrective formula which should be applied to "raw" η. Still another corrective formula applies when the class-intervals are large and the number of columns and rows is small.

Test for Linearity of Correlation. It is often difficult to tell, even by the graphic treatment of correlation discussed in the previous chapter, whether correlation is linear or non-linear.

TABLE 81

CALCULATION OF η_{yx} IN A TWO-WAY TABLE

X score

Y score	25	30	35	40	45	50	55	60	65	70	F_y	η	$F_y\eta$	$F_y\eta^2$
75............										1	1	6	6	36
70............									1	1	2	5	10	50
65............		1							4		5	4	20	80
60............	2	2					3		4		11	3	33	99
55............	4				1	2	2				9	2	18	36
50............	2		2	1		1	4	3			13	1	13	13
45............		4	3	3	3	2	4	3			22	0	0	0
40............			6	2	4	5					17	−1	−17	17
35............				4	4						8	−2	−16	32
F_x............	8	7	11	10	12	10	10	9	9	2	88		67	363
$\overline{Y}_x$............	55	52.1	43.2	40.5	40.8	45	49	51.7	63.3	72.5				
$(\overline{Y}_x - M_y)$...	6.2	3.3	−5.6	−8.3	−8	−3.8	0.2	2.9	14.5	23.7				
$(\overline{Y}_x - M_y)^2$...	38.44	10.89	31.36	68.89	64	14.44	.04	8.41	210.25	561.69				
$F_x(\overline{Y}_x - M_y)^2$...	307.52	76.23	344.96	688.9	768	144.4	0.4	75.69	1892.25	1123.38				

$C_y = \dfrac{67}{88} = 0.76$

class-interval
= 3.80 units
$+ 45$

$M_y = 48.8$

$$\sigma_{my} = \sqrt{\frac{\Sigma F_x(\overline{Y}_x - M_y)^2}{N}} = \sqrt{\frac{5421.73}{88}} = 7.85$$

$$\sigma_y = \left[\sqrt{\frac{363}{88} - (0.76)^2}\right] \times 5 = 9.40$$

$$\eta_{yx} = \frac{\sigma_{my}}{\sigma_y} = \frac{7.85}{9.40} = 0.84$$

TABLE 82

CALCULATION OF η_{xy} IN A TWO-WAY TABLE

X score

Y score	25	30	35	40	45	50	55	60	65	70	F_y	$\overline{X}_y$	$\overline{X}_y - M_x$	$(\overline{X}_y - M_x)^2$	$F_y(\overline{X}_y - M_x)^2$
75.........										1	1	70	24	576	576
70.........									1	1	2	67.5	21.5	462.25	924.50
65.........		1							4		5	58	12	144	720
60.........	2	2					3		4		11	50	4	16	176
55.........	4				1	2	2				9	39.4	−6.6	43.56	392.04
50.........	2		2	1		1	4	3			13	46.9	0.9	0.81	10.53
45.........		4	3	3	3	2	4	3			22	44.5	−1.5	2.25	49.5
40.........			6	2	4	5					17	42.4	−3.6	12.96	220.32
35.........				4	4						8	42.5	−3.5	12.25	98.0

3166.89

	25	30	35	40	45	50	55	60	65	70	
F_x.........	8	7	11	10	12	10	10	9	9	2	88
ξ.........	−4	−3	−2	−1	0	1	2	3	4	5	
$F_x\xi$.........	−32	−21	−22	−10	0	10	20	27	36	10	
$F_x\xi^2$.......	128	63	44	10	0	10	40	81	144	50	

$C_x = \dfrac{9}{44} = 0.2$ class-interval

= 1.0 units
$+45$

$M_x = 46$

$$\sigma_{mx} = \sqrt{\frac{3166.89}{88}} = 5.99$$

$$\sigma_x = \left(\sqrt{\frac{285}{44} - (0.2)^2}\right) \times 5 = 12.70$$

$$\eta_{xy} = \frac{\sigma_{mx}}{\sigma_x} = \frac{5.99}{12.70} = 0.47$$

Hence, in cases of doubt, it is advisable to calculate both r and η. If the difference between them is slight, the correlation can be regarded as approximately linear.

The question naturally arises as to what difference between r and η can be considered "slight." Blakeman has given a test which measures this fact. We mention here only the shortened form of this test, which states that correlation can be considered approximately linear if

$$N(\eta^2 - r^2) < 11.37$$

This test is applicable only when $\eta^2 - r^2$ is small in comparison with r, or when η and r are both small.

Ex. 13. Using the results of Ex. 12 of this chapter, and the correlation coefficients which you computed in the previous chapter, use Blakeman's short test for those tables to which it is applicable.

Partial Correlation. In making a correlation study, incomplete analysis may lead to the conclusion that a decided relationship exists between two measures, when this relationship is partly or entirely due to other factors which influence both measures.

For example, suppose that a correlation study is made of the relationship between ability in chemistry and ability in physics, by testing a mixed group consisting of third- and fourth-year high-school students and college freshmen. Such a study might not reveal the true degree of relationship, as a result of the influence, on the scores obtained, of such extraneous factors as previous mathematical or scientific training of students and differences in maturity and general background.

To obtain more valid results, the tests should be given to a group of students of the same maturity, with the same general background and previous scientific training.

Sometimes it is impossible to control the extraneous factors in this way, and mathematics offers a different method of solution to such correlation problems. The use of "partial" correlation formulas rules out, by mathematical means, the effect of undesired factors.

For a discussion of partial correlation we refer the student to more advanced works, but warn him at this time to be cautious in the use of such correlation methods as we have discussed here.

Ex. 14. Bring in illustrative material from educational periodicals to show the applications of correlation methods to testing.

Summary. In this chapter we have dealt with various applications of correlation theory to *testing*, in particular the measurement of *reliability* and *validity*. We have also discussed various corrections which it is customary to apply to a coefficient of correlation, and have given a brief treatment of curvilinear correlation.

REFERENCES

GENERAL TEXTS

GARRETT, HENRY E. Statistics in Psychology and Education. Longmans, Green & Co.

HOLZINGER, KARL J. Statistical Methods for Students in Education. Ginn & Co.

OTIS, ARTHUR S. Statistical Method in Educational Measurement. World Book Co.

RUGG, HAROLD O. Statistical Methods Applied to Educational Problems. Houghton Mifflin Co.

THURSTONE, L. L. Fundamentals of Statistics. Macmillan Co.

WILLIAMS, J. H. Graphic Methods in Education. Houghton Mifflin Co.

MORE ADVANCED BOOKS

BROWN, W., and THOMSON, G. Essentials of Mental Measurement. Cambridge University Press, London.

KELLEY, TRUMAN L. Statistical Method. Macmillan Co.

MATHEMATICAL TEXTS

BURGESS, ROBERT W. Introduction to the Mathematics of Statistics. Houghton Mifflin Co.

FORSYTH, C. H. Mathematical Analysis of Statistics. John Wiley & Sons.

JONES, D. CARADOG. First Course in Statistics. G. Bell & Sons, London.

YULE, G. UDNY. Introduction to the Theory of Statistics. Charles Griffin & Co., London.

APPENDIX

LIST OF FORMULAS USED IN THIS TEXT

$$Mdn = l + \frac{\frac{N}{2} - b}{f} \times i$$

or

Median
$$Mdn = u - \frac{\frac{N}{2} - a}{f} \times i$$

Correction to mean
$$c = \frac{\Sigma F\xi}{N}$$

Semi-interquartile range
$$Q = \frac{Q_3 - Q_1}{2}$$

Mean deviation
$$\text{M.D.} = \frac{\Sigma|x|}{N}$$

Standard deviation
$$\sigma = \sqrt{\frac{\Sigma x^2}{N}}$$

Standard deviation for grouped scores
$$\sigma = \sqrt{\frac{\Sigma F x^2}{N}}$$

or
$$\sigma = \left[\sqrt{\frac{\Sigma F\xi^2}{N} - c^2} \right] \times i$$

Coefficient of variation
$$V = \frac{100\sigma}{M}$$

Standard score
$$\text{Standard score} = \frac{x}{\sigma}$$

Skewness
$$\text{Skewness} = \frac{3(M - Mdn)}{\sigma}$$

Standard error of the mean
$$\sigma_M = \frac{\sigma_s}{\sqrt{N}}$$

Standard error of the median
$$\sigma_{Mdn} = \frac{5}{4} \frac{\sigma_s}{\sqrt{N}}$$

Standard error of the standard deviation	σ_σ	$= \dfrac{\sigma_s}{\sqrt{2N}}$
Standard error of the semi-interquartile range	σ_Q	$= 1.11\dfrac{\sigma_s}{\sqrt{2N}}$

or

$$\sigma_Q = 1.65\frac{Q_s}{\sqrt{2N}}$$

Probable error of the median

$$\text{P.E.}_{Mdn} = \frac{5}{4}\frac{Q_s}{\sqrt{2N}}$$

Standard error of a difference

$$\sigma_d = \sqrt{\sigma_1^2 + \sigma_2^2 - 2r\sigma_1\sigma_2}$$

Correlation coefficient

$$r = \frac{\Sigma xy}{\sqrt{\Sigma x^2 \Sigma y^2}}$$

or

$$r = \frac{\dfrac{\Sigma \xi\eta}{N} - c_x c_y}{\sigma_x \sigma_y}$$

Regression lines

$$y = r\frac{\sigma_y}{\sigma_x}x$$

$$x = r\frac{\sigma_x}{\sigma_y}y$$

Standard error of a correlation coefficient

$$\sigma_r = \frac{1 - r^2}{\sqrt{N}}$$

Standard errors of estimate in predictions from regression equations

$$\sigma_{(\text{est. } Y)} = \sigma_y\sqrt{1 - r^2}$$
$$\sigma_{(\text{est. } X)} = \sigma_x\sqrt{1 - r^2}$$

Spearman-Brown prophecy formula

$$r_x = \frac{Nr}{1 + (N - 1)r}$$

Correlation coefficient corrected for attenuation

$$r_{AB} = \frac{\sqrt{r_{A_1B_2}r_{A_2B_1}}}{\sqrt{r_{A_1A_2}r_{B_1B_2}}}$$

or

$$r_{AB} = \frac{r_{A_1B_1}}{\sqrt{r_{A_1A_2}r_{B_1B_2}}}$$

Correction of correlation coefficient for heterogeneity

$$\frac{\sigma}{\Sigma} = \frac{\sqrt{1-R}}{\sqrt{1-r}}$$

Correlation ratio

$$\eta_{yx} = \frac{\sigma_{my}}{\sigma_y}$$

where

$$\sigma_{my} = \sqrt{\frac{\Sigma F_x(\overline{Y}_x - M_y)^2}{N}}$$

and

$$\eta_{xy} = \frac{\sigma_{mx}}{\sigma_x}$$

where

$$\sigma_{mx} = \sqrt{\frac{\Sigma F_y(\overline{X}_y - M_x)^2}{N}}$$

Blakeman's short test for linearity

$$N(\eta^2 - r^2) < 11.37$$

NOTE I

DERIVATION OF THE FORMULA $c = \dfrac{\Sigma F\xi}{N}$

If $X_1, X_2, X_3, \ldots X_N$ represent a set of scores, their mean is

$$M = \frac{X_1 + X_2 + X_3 + \ldots + X_N}{N}$$

or, in the Σ notation,

$$M = \frac{\Sigma X}{N}$$

If the scores are grouped into a frequency distribution, then we have

Score   Frequency

Score	Frequency	
X_1	F_1	$M = \dfrac{F_1X_1 + F_2X_2 + F_3X_3 + \ldots + F_kX_k}{N}$
X_2	F_2	or
.	.	$M = \dfrac{\Sigma FX}{N}$
X_k	F_k	

If an estimated mean E is used, then we have

Score	Frequency	Score	Frequency
$X_1 = E + \xi_1$	F_1	$F_1E +$	$F_1\xi_1$
$X_2 = E + \xi_2$	F_2	$F_2E +$	$F_2\xi_2$
$X_3 = E + \xi_3$	F_3	$F_3E +$	$F_3\xi_3$
$X_k = E + \xi_k$	F_k	$F_kE +$	$F_k\xi_k$

$$M = \frac{F_1E + F_2E + \ldots + F_kE + F_1\xi_1 + F_2\xi_2 + \ldots + F_k\xi_k}{N}$$

$$= \frac{(F_1 + F_2 + \ldots + F_k)E + (F_1\xi_1 + F_2\xi_2 + \ldots + F_k\xi_k)}{N}$$

$$= \frac{NE}{N} + \frac{F_1\xi_1 + F_2\xi_2 + \ldots + F_k\xi_k}{N} = E + \frac{\Sigma F\xi}{N}$$

Hence the correction $c = \dfrac{\Sigma F\xi}{N}$

NOTE II

Derivation of the Formula $\sigma = \sqrt{\dfrac{\Sigma F \xi^2}{N} - c^2}$

If scores are grouped, we have seen in Chapter III

$$\sigma = \sqrt{\frac{\Sigma F x^2}{N}}$$

where x represents deviation from the mean.

Now

$$x = X - M$$
$$M = E + c$$
$$\therefore \ x = X - E - c$$
$$\xi = X - E$$
$$\therefore \ x = (X - E) - c = \xi - c$$

where X represents a score.

M represents the mean.

E represents the estimated mean.

c represents the correction to the estimated mean.

ξ represents deviation from the estimated mean.

Hence

$$x_1 = \xi_1 - c \qquad x_1{}^2 = \xi_1{}^2 - 2c\xi_1 + c^2$$
$$x_2 = \xi_2 - c \qquad x_2{}^2 = \xi_2{}^2 - 2c\xi_2 + c^2$$
$$\dotfill$$
$$x_k = \xi_k - c \qquad x_k{}^2 = \xi_k{}^2 - 2c\xi_k + c^2$$
$$F_1 x_1{}^2 = F_1 \xi_1{}^2 - 2cF_1\xi_1 + F_1 c^2$$
$$F_2 x_2{}^2 = F_2 \xi_2{}^2 - 2cF_2\xi_2 + F_2 c^2$$
$$\dotfill$$
$$F_k x_k{}^2 = F_k \xi_k{}^2 - 2cF_k\xi_k + F_k c^2$$

Adding these equations, we have

$$F_1 x_1{}^2 + F_2 x_2{}^2 + \ldots + F_k x_k{}^2 = (F_1 \xi_1{}^2 + F_2 \xi_2{}^2 + \ldots$$
$$+ F_k \xi_k{}^2) - 2c(F_1\xi_1 + F_2\xi_2 + \ldots + F_k\xi_k)$$
$$+ c^2(F_1 + F_2 + \ldots + F_k)$$

or

$$\Sigma F x^2 = \Sigma F \xi^2 - 2c\Sigma F \xi + c^2 N$$

Dividing both sides by N, we have

$$\frac{\Sigma F x^2}{N} = \frac{\Sigma F \xi^2}{N} - 2c\frac{\Sigma F \xi}{N} + c^2$$

$$= \frac{\Sigma F \xi^2}{N} - 2c^2 + c^2$$

$$= \frac{\Sigma F \xi^2}{N} - c^2$$

$$\therefore \sigma = \sqrt{\frac{\Sigma F x^2}{N}} = \sqrt{\frac{\Sigma F \xi^2}{N} - c^2}$$

NOTE III

THE METHOD OF LEAST SQUARES

Fundamental Principle. After the *type* of curve of best fit for a given set of points has been determined, *the constants in this equation should be chosen so as to make the sum of the squares of the residuals of the points a minimum.*

Definition. By the *residual* of a point is meant the difference between the actual and graduated values of the ordinate.

Thus, let us refer to the exercise worked in the text by the method of moments.

The sum of the squares of the residuals is

$$S = (m + b - 3)^2 + (2m + b - 2)^2 + (3m + b - 4)^2 \\ + (4m + b - 6)^2 + (5m + b - 5)^2$$

From the calculus, the conditions for a minimum are

$$\frac{\partial S}{\partial m} = 0 \quad \frac{\partial S}{\partial b} = 0$$

$$\frac{\partial S}{\partial m} = 2(m + b - 3) + 4(2m + b - 2) + 6(3m + b - 4)$$

$$+ 8(4m + b - 6) + 10(5m + b - 5) = 0$$

$$\frac{\partial S}{\partial b} = 2(m + b - 3) + 2(2m + b - 2) + 2(3m + b - 4)$$

$$+ 2(4m + b - 6) + 2(5m + b - 5) = 0$$

Dividing each equation by 2, and collecting terms, we have

$$55m + 15b = 68$$
$$15m + 5b = 20$$

These are the same equations obtained by the method of moments, and hence the values of m and b, and the equation of the line of best fit, will be the same.

In general, in fitting curves other than a straight line by the method of moments and method of least squares, respectively, the results will differ.

Ex. Work Exs. 3, 4, 5, 6, 7 of Chapter VII by the method of least squares.

NOTE IV

DERIVATION OF THE EQUATION OF THE LINE OF BEST FIT
$Y = mX + b$ FOR A SET OF POINTS

Derivation by Method of Moments. We have seen, in Chapter VII, that the point whose coordinates are the mean of the X's and the mean of the Y's, $\left(\dfrac{\Sigma x}{n}, \dfrac{\Sigma y}{n}\right)$ lies on the line of best fit, $Y = mX + b$. If we take this point as origin, the line of best fit takes the specially simple form, $y = mx$, where x and y, the new coordinates, represent deviations from the respective means.

We have

Given points		Graduated points	
x	y	x	y
x_1	y_1	x_1	mx_1
x_2	y_2	x_2	mx_2
..	..	..	..
..	..	..	..
..	..	..	..
x_n	y_n	x_n	mx_n

To obtain the value of m in the equation $y = mx$, we equate zeroth moments and obtain

$$y_1 + y_2 + \ldots + y_n = m(x_1 + x_2 + \ldots + x_n)$$

But, by virtue of the origin chosen,

$$\frac{x_1 + x_2 + \ldots + x_n}{n} = 0$$

and

$$\frac{y_1 + y_2 + \ldots + y_n}{n} = 0$$

Hence

$$x_1 + x_2 + \ldots + x_n = 0$$

and

$$y_1 + y_2 + \ldots + y_n = 0$$

and the above equation becomes the identity

$$0 = m \cdot 0$$
$$0 = 0$$

Equating first moments, we obtain

$$x_1y_1 + x_2y_2 + \ldots + x_ny_n = m(x_1^2 + x_2^2 + \ldots + x_n^2)$$

and

$$m = \frac{x_1y_1 + x_2y_2 + \ldots + x_ny_n}{x_1^2 + x_2^2 + \ldots + x_n^2}$$

or

$$m = \frac{\Sigma xy}{\Sigma x^2}$$

Dividing numerator and denominator of this fraction by n, we have

$$m = \frac{\dfrac{\Sigma xy}{n}}{\dfrac{\Sigma x^2}{n}}$$

Now

$$\sigma_x = \sqrt{\frac{\Sigma x^2}{n}}$$

Let

$$p = \frac{\Sigma xy}{n}$$

Then

$$m = \frac{p}{\sigma_x^2}$$

and the line of best fit is

$$y = \frac{p}{\sigma_x^2} x$$

Dividing both sides of this equation by σ_y, we have

$$\frac{y}{\sigma_y} = \frac{p}{\sigma_x \sigma_y} \frac{x}{\sigma_x}$$

Now, in Chapter VII we have taken

$$r = \frac{\Sigma xy}{\sqrt{\Sigma x^2 \Sigma y^2}}$$

Dividing numerator and denominator by n, we have

$$r = \frac{\dfrac{\Sigma xy}{n}}{\sqrt{\dfrac{\Sigma x^2}{n}} \sqrt{\dfrac{\Sigma y^2}{n}}} = \frac{p}{\sigma_x \sigma_y}$$

Hence, the quantity $\dfrac{p}{\sigma_x \sigma_y}$ is the *correlation coefficient* r, and the above equation becomes

$$\frac{y}{\sigma_y} = r\frac{x}{\sigma_x}$$

or

$$y = r\frac{\sigma_y}{\sigma_x}x$$

To derive this equation by the *method of least squares*, we have the condition that

$$S = (mx_1 - y_1)^2 + (mx_2 - y_2)^2 + \ldots + (mx_n - y_n)^2$$

should be a minimum.

$$\frac{dS}{dm} = 2x_1(mx_1 - y_1) + 2x_2(mx_2 - y_2) + \ldots + 2x_n(mx_n - y_n) = 0$$

$$m(x_1^2 + x_2^2 + \ldots + x_n^2) - (x_1y_1 + x_2y_2 + \ldots + x_ny_n) = 0$$

or, once more

$$m = \frac{\Sigma xy}{\Sigma x^2}$$

NOTE V

DERIVATION OF THE FORMULA FOR THE CORRELATION COEFFICIENT

$$r = \frac{\dfrac{\Sigma \xi \eta}{N} - c_x c_y}{\sigma_x \sigma_y}$$

We have seen in Note IV that $r = \dfrac{p}{\sigma_x \sigma_y}$

where $$p = \frac{\Sigma xy}{N}$$

and x and y are deviations from M_x and M_y respectively.

Now, if estimated means E_x and E_y are used,

$$M_x = E_x + c_x$$
$$M_y = E_y + c_y$$

and

$$x = X - M_x = X - E_x - c_x = \xi - c_x$$
$$y = Y - M_y = Y - E_y - c_y = \eta - c_y$$

where ξ and η represent deviations from E_x and E_y respectively.

Then
$$p = \frac{\Sigma xy}{N} = \frac{\Sigma(\xi - c_x)(\eta - c_y)}{N}$$

$$= \frac{\Sigma(\xi \eta - c_x \eta - c_y \xi + c_x c_y)}{N}$$

$$= \frac{\Sigma \xi \eta}{N} - c_x \frac{\Sigma \eta}{N} - c_y \frac{\Sigma \xi}{N} + \frac{N c_x c_y}{N}$$

$$= \frac{\Sigma \xi \eta}{N} - c_x c_y - c_y c_x + c_x c_y$$

$$= \frac{\Sigma \xi \eta}{N} - c_x c_y$$

Hence
$$r = \frac{\dfrac{\Sigma \xi \eta}{N} - c_x c_y}{\sigma_x \sigma_y}$$

TABLE OF SQUARES AND SQUARE ROOTS

n	n^2	$\sqrt{n}$	n	n^2	$\sqrt{n}$	n	n^2	$\sqrt{n}$	n	n^2	$\sqrt{n}$
1	1	1.	51	2601	7.1414	101	10201	10.0499	151	22801	12.2882
2	4	1.414	52	2704	7.2111	102	10404	10.0995	152	23104	12.3288
3	9	1.732	53	2809	7.2801	103	10609	10.1489	153	23409	12.3693
4	16	2.000	54	2916	7.3485	104	10816	10.1980	154	23716	12.4097
5	25	2.236	55	3025	7.4162	105	11025	10.2470	155	24025	12.4499
6	36	2.449	56	3136	7.4833	106	11236	10.2956	156	24336	12.4900
7	49	2.646	57	3249	7.5498	107	11449	10.3441	157	24649	12.5300
8	64	2.828	58	3364	7.6158	108	11664	10.3923	158	24964	12.5698
9	81	3.000	59	3481	7.6811	109	11881	10.4403	159	25281	12.6095
10	100	3.162	60	3600	7.7460	110	12100	10.4881	160	25600	12.6491
11	121	3.3166	61	3721	7.8102	111	12321	10.5357	161	25921	12.6886
12	144	3.4641	62	3844	7.8740	112	12544	10.5830	162	26244	12.7279
13	169	3.6056	63	3969	7.9373	113	12769	10.6301	163	26569	12.7671
14	196	3.7417	64	4096	8.0000	114	12996	10.6771	164	26896	12.8062
15	225	3.8730	65	4225	8.0623	115	13225	10.7238	165	27225	12.8452
16	256	4.0000	66	4356	8.1240	116	13456	10.7703	166	27556	12.8841
17	289	4.1231	67	4489	8.1854	117	13689	10.8167	167	27889	12.9228
18	324	4.2426	68	4624	8.2462	118	13924	10.8628	168	28224	12.9615
19	361	4.3589	69	4761	8.3066	119	14161	10.9087	169	28561	13.0000
20	400	4.4721	70	4900	8.3666	120	14400	10.9545	170	28900	13.0384
21	441	4.5826	71	5041	8.4261	121	14641	11.0000	171	29241	13.0767
22	484	4.6904	72	5184	8.4853	122	14884	11.0454	172	29584	13.1149
23	529	4.7958	73	5329	8.5440	123	15129	11.0905	173	29929	13.1529
24	576	4.8990	74	5476	8.6023	124	15376	11.1355	174	30276	13.1909
25	625	5.0000	75	5625	8.6603	125	15625	11.1803	175	30625	13.2288
26	676	5.0990	76	5776	8.7178	126	15876	11.2250	176	30976	13.2665
27	729	5.1962	77	5929	8.7750	127	16129	11.2694	177	31329	13.3041
28	784	5.2915	78	6084	8.8318	128	16384	11.3137	178	31684	13.3417
29	841	5.3852	79	6241	8.8882	129	16641	11.3578	179	32041	13.3791
30	900	5.4772	80	6400	8.9443	130	16900	11.4018	180	32400	13.4164
31	961	5.5678	81	6561	9.0000	131	17161	11.4455	181	32761	13.4536
32	1024	5.6569	82	6724	9.0554	132	17424	11.4891	182	33124	13.4907
33	1089	5.7446	83	6889	9.1104	133	17689	11.5326	183	33489	13.5277
34	1156	5.8310	84	7056	9.1652	134	17956	11.5758	184	33856	13.5647
35	1225	5.9161	85	7225	9.2195	135	18225	11.6190	185	34225	13.6015
36	1296	6.0000	86	7396	9.2736	136	18496	11.6619	186	34596	13.6382
37	1369	6.0828	87	7569	9.3274	137	18769	11.7047	187	34969	13.6748
38	1444	6.1644	88	7744	9.3808	138	19044	11.7473	188	35344	13.7113
39	1521	6.2450	89	7921	9.4340	139	19321	11.7898	189	35721	13.7477
40	1600	6.3246	90	8100	9.4868	140	19600	11.8322	190	36100	13.7840
41	1681	6.4031	91	8281	9.5394	141	19881	11.8743	191	36481	13.8203
42	1764	6.4807	92	8464	9.5917	142	20164	11.9164	192	36864	13.8564
43	1849	6.5574	93	8649	9.6437	143	20449	11.9583	193	37249	13.8924
44	1936	6.6332	94	8836	9.6954	144	20736	12.0000	194	37636	13.9284
45	2025	6.7082	95	9025	9.7468	145	21025	12.0416	195	38025	13.9642
46	2116	6.7823	96	9216	9.7980	146	21316	12.0830	196	38416	14.0000
47	2209	6.8557	97	9409	9.8489	147	21609	12.1244	197	38809	14.0357
48	2304	6.9282	98	9604	9.8995	148	21904	12.1655	198	39204	14.0712
49	2401	7.0000	99	9801	9.9499	149	22201	12.2066	199	39601	14.1067
50	2500	7.0711	100	10000	10.0000	150	22500	12.2474	200	40000	14.1421

n	n^2	$\sqrt{n}$	n	n^2	$\sqrt{n}$	n	n^2	$\sqrt{n}$	n	n^2	$\sqrt{n}$
201	40401	14.1774	251	63001	15.8430	301	90601	17.3494	351	123201	18.7350
202	40804	14.2127	252	63504	15.8745	302	91204	17.3781	352	123904	18.7617
203	41209	14.2478	253	64009	15.9060	303	91809	17.4069	353	124609	18.7883
204	41616	14.2829	254	64516	15.9374	304	92416	17.4356	354	125316	18.8149
205	42025	14.3178	255	65025	15.9687	305	93025	17.4642	355	126025	18.8414
206	42436	14.3527	256	65536	16.0000	306	93636	17.4929	356	126736	18.8680
207	42849	14.3875	257	66049	16.0312	307	94249	17.5214	357	127449	18.8944
208	43264	14.4222	258	66564	16.0624	308	94864	17.5499	358	128164	18.9209
209	43681	14.4568	259	67081	16.0935	309	95481	17.5784	359	128881	18.9473
210	44100	14.4914	260	67600	16.1245	310	96100	17.6068	360	129600	18.9737
211	44521	14.5258	261	68121	16.1555	311	96721	17.6352	361	130321	19.0000
212	44944	14.5602	262	68644	16.1864	312	97344	17.6635	362	131044	19.0263
213	45369	14.5945	263	69169	16.2173	313	97969	17.6918	363	131769	19.0526
214	45796	14.6287	264	69696	16.2481	314	98596	17.7200	364	132496	19.0788
215	46225	14.6629	265	70225	16.2788	315	99225	17.7482	365	133225	19.1050
216	46656	14.6969	266	70756	16.3095	316	99856	17.7764	366	133956	19.1311
217	47089	14.7309	267	71289	16.3401	317	100489	17.8045	367	134689	19.1572
218	47524	14.7648	268	71824	16.3707	318	101124	17.8326	368	135424	19.1833
219	47961	14.7986	269	72361	16.4012	319	101761	17.8606	369	136161	19.2094
220	48400	14.8324	270	72900	16.4317	320	102400	17.8885	370	136900	19.2354
221	48841	14.8661	271	73441	16.4621	321	103041	17.9165	371	137641	19.2614
222	49284	14.8997	272	73984	16.4924	322	103684	17.9444	372	138384	19.2873
223	49729	14.9332	273	74529	16.5227	323	104329	17.9722	373	139129	19.3132
224	50176	14.9666	274	75076	16.5529	324	104976	18.0000	374	139876	19.3391
225	50625	15.0000	275	75625	16.5831	325	105625	18.0278	375	140625	19.3649
226	51076	15.0333	276	76176	16.6132	326	106276	18.0555	376	141376	19.3907
227	51529	15.0665	277	76729	16.6433	327	106929	18.0831	377	142129	19.4165
228	51984	15.0997	278	77284	16.6733	328	107584	18.1108	378	142884	19.4422
229	52441	15.1327	279	77841	16.7033	329	108241	18.1384	379	143641	19.4679
230	52900	15.1658	280	78400	16.7332	330	180900	18.1659	380	144400	19.4936
231	53361	15.1987	281	78961	16.7631	331	109561	18.1934	381	145161	19.5192
232	53824	15.2315	282	79524	16.7929	332	110224	18.2209	382	145924	19.5448
233	54289	15.2643	283	80089	16.8226	333	110889	18.2483	383	146689	19.5704
234	54756	15.2971	284	80656	16.8523	334	111556	18.2757	384	147456	19.5959
235	55225	15.3297	285	81225	16.8819	335	112225	18.3030	385	148225	19.6214
236	55696	15.3623	286	81796	16.9115	336	112896	18.3303	386	148996	19.6469
237	56169	15.3948	287	82369	16.9411	337	113569	18.3576	387	149769	19.6723
238	56644	15.4272	288	82944	16.9706	338	114244	18.3848	388	150544	19.6977
239	57121	15.4596	289	83521	17.0000	339	114921	18.4120	389	151321	19.7231
240	57600	15.4919	290	84100	17.0294	340	115600	18.4391	390	152100	19.7484
241	58081	15.5242	291	84681	17.0587	341	116281	18.4662	391	152881	19.7737
242	58564	15.5563	292	85264	17.0880	342	116964	18.4932	392	153664	19.7990
243	59049	15.5885	293	85849	17.1172	343	117649	18.5203	393	154449	19.8242
244	59536	15.6205	294	86436	17.1464	344	118336	18.5472	394	155236	19.8494
245	60025	15.6525	295	87025	17.1756	345	119025	18.5742	395	156025	19.8746
246	60516	15.6844	296	87616	17.2047	346	119716	18.6011	396	156816	19.8997
247	61009	15.7162	297	88209	17.2337	347	120409	18.6279	397	157609	19.9249
248	61504	15.7480	298	88804	17.2627	348	121104	18.6548	398	158404	19.9499
249	62001	15.7797	299	89401	17.2916	349	121801	18.6815	399	159201	19.9750
250	62500	15.8114	300	90000	17.3205	350	122500	18.7083	400	160000	20.0000

n	n^2	$\sqrt{n}$	n	n^2	$\sqrt{n}$	n	n^2	$\sqrt{n}$	n	n^2	$\sqrt{n}$
401	160801	20.0250	451	203401	21.2368	501	251001	22.3830	551	303601	23.4734
402	161604	20.0499	452	204304	21.2603	502	252004	22.4054	552	304704	23.4947
403	162409	20.0749	453	205209	21.2838	503	253009	22.4277	553	305809	23.5160
404	163216	20.0998	454	206116	21.3073	504	254016	22.4499	554	306916	23.5372
405	164025	20.1246	455	207025	21.3307	505	255025	22.4722	555	308025	23.5584
406	164836	20.1494	456	207936	21.3542	506	256036	22.4944	556	309136	23.5797
407	165649	20.1742	457	208849	21.3776	507	257049	22.5167	557	310249	23.6008
408	166464	20.1990	458	209764	21.4009	508	258064	22.5389	558	311364	23.6220
409	167281	20.2237	459	210681	21.4243	509	259081	22.5610	559	312481	23.6432
410	168100	20.2485	460	211600	21.4476	510	260100	22.5832	560	313600	23.6643
411	168921	20.2731	461	212521	21.4709	511	261121	22.6053	561	314721	23.6854
412	169744	20.2978	462	213444	21.4942	512	262144	22.6274	562	315844	23.7065
413	170569	20.3224	463	214369	21.5174	513	263169	22.6495	563	316969	23.7276
414	171396	20.3470	464	215296	21.5407	514	264196	22.6716	564	318096	23.7487
415	172225	20.3715	465	216225	21.5639	515	265225	22.6936	565	319225	23.7697
416	173056	20.3961	466	217156	21.5870	516	266256	22.7156	566	320356	23.7908
417	173889	20.4206	467	218089	21.6102	517	267289	22.7376	567	321489	23.8118
418	174724	20.4450	468	219024	21.6333	518	268324	22.7596	568	322624	23.8328
419	175561	20.4695	469	219961	21.6564	519	269361	22.7816	569	323761	23.8537
420	176400	20.4939	470	220900	21.6795	520	270400	22.8035	570	324900	23.8747
421	177241	20.5183	471	221841	21.7025	521	271441	22.8254	571	326041	23.8956
422	178084	20.5426	472	222784	21.7256	522	272484	22.8473	572	327184	23.9165
423	178929	20.5670	473	223729	21.7486	523	273529	22.8692	573	328329	23.9374
424	179776	20.5913	474	224676	21.7715	524	274576	22.8910	574	329476	23.9583
425	180625	20.6155	475	225625	21.7945	525	275625	22.9129	575	330625	23.9792
426	181476	20.6398	476	226576	21.8174	526	276676	22.9347	576	331776	24.0000
427	182329	20.6640	477	227529	21.8403	527	277729	22.9565	577	332929	24.0208
428	183184	20.6882	478	228484	21.8632	528	278784	22.9783	578	334084	24.0416
429	184041	20.7123	479	229441	21.8861	529	279841	23.0000	579	335241	24.0624
430	184900	20.7364	480	230400	21.9089	530	280900	23.0217	580	336400	24.0832
431	185761	20.7605	481	231361	21.9317	531	281961	23.0434	581	337561	24.1039
432	186624	20.7846	482	232324	21.9545	532	283024	23.0651	582	338724	24.1247
433	187489	20.8087	483	233289	21.9773	533	284089	23.0868	583	339889	24.1454
434	188356	20.8327	484	234256	22.0000	534	285156	23.1084	584	341056	24.1661
435	189225	20.8567	485	235225	22.0227	535	286225	23.1301	585	342225	24.1868
436	190096	20.8806	486	236196	22.0454	536	287296	23.1517	586	343396	24.2074
437	190969	20.9045	487	237169	22.0681	537	288369	23.1733	587	344569	24.2281
438	191844	20.9284	488	238144	22.0907	538	289444	23.1948	588	345744	24.2487
439	192721	20.9523	489	239121	22.1133	539	290521	23.2164	589	346921	24.2693
440	193600	20.9762	490	240100	22.1359	540	291600	23.2379	590	348100	24.2899
441	194481	21.0000	491	241081	22.1585	541	292681	23.2594	591	349281	24.3105
442	195364	21.0238	492	242064	22.1811	542	293764	23.2809	592	350464	24.3311
443	196249	21.0476	493	243049	22.2036	543	294849	23.3024	593	351649	24.3516
444	197136	21.0713	494	244036	22.2261	544	295936	23.3238	594	352836	24.3721
445	198025	21.0950	495	245025	22.2486	545	297025	23.3452	595	354025	24.3926
446	198916	21.1187	496	246016	22.2711	546	298116	23.3666	596	355216	24.4131
447	199809	21.1424	497	247009	22.2935	547	299209	23.3880	597	356409	24.4336
448	200704	21.1660	498	248004	22.3159	548	300304	23.4094	598	357604	24.4540
449	201601	21.1896	499	249001	22.3383	549	301401	23.4307	599	358801	24.4745
450	202500	21.2132	500	250000	22.3607	550	302500	23.4521	600	360000	24.4949

n	n^2	$\sqrt{n}$	n	n^2	$\sqrt{n}$	n	n^2	$\sqrt{n}$	n	n^2	$\sqrt{n}$
601	361201	24.5153	651	423801	25.5147	701	491401	26.4764	751	564001	27.4044
602	362404	24.5357	652	425104	25.5343	702	492804	26.4953	752	565504	27.4226
603	363609	24.5561	653	426409	25.5539	703	494209	26.5141	753	567009	27.4408
604	364816	24.5764	654	427716	25.5734	704	495616	26.5330	754	568516	27.4591
605	366025	24.5967	655	429025	25.5930	705	497025	26.5518	755	570025	27.4773
606	367236	24.6171	656	430336	25.6125	706	498436	26.5707	756	571536	27.4955
607	368449	24.6374	657	431649	25.6320	707	499849	26.5895	757	573049	27.5136
608	369664	24.6577	658	432964	25.6515	708	501264	26.6083	758	574564	27.5318
609	370881	24.6779	659	434281	25.6710	709	502681	26.6271	759	576081	27.5500
610	372100	24.6982	660	435600	25.6905	710	504100	26.6458	760	577600	27.5681
611	373321	24.7184	661	436921	25.7099	711	505521	26.6646	761	579121	27.5862
612	374544	24.7386	662	438244	25.7294	712	506944	26.6833	762	580644	27.6043
613	375769	24.7588	663	439569	25.7488	713	508369	26.7021	763	582169	27.6225
614	376996	24.7790	664	440896	25.7682	714	509796	26.7208	764	583696	27.6405
615	378225	24.7992	665	442225	25.7876	715	511225	26.7395	765	585225	27.6586
616	379456	24.8193	666	443556	25.8070	716	512656	26.7582	766	586756	27.6767
617	380689	24.8395	667	444889	25.8263	717	514089	26.7769	767	588289	27.6948
618	381924	24.8596	668	446224	25.8457	718	515524	26.7955	768	589824	27.7128
619	383161	24.8797	669	447561	25.8650	719	516961	26.8142	769	591361	27.7308
620	384400	24.8998	670	448900	25.8844	720	518400	26.8328	770	592900	27.7489
621	385641	24.9199	671	450241	25.9037	721	519841	26.8514	771	594441	27.7669
622	386884	24.9399	672	451584	25.9230	722	521284	26.8701	772	595984	27.7849
623	388129	24.9600	673	452929	25.9422	723	522729	26.8887	773	597529	27.8029
624	389376	24.9800	674	454276	25.9615	724	524176	26.9072	774	599076	27.8209
625	390625	25.0000	675	455625	25.9808	725	525625	26.9258	775	600625	27.8388
626	391876	25.0200	676	456976	26.0000	726	527076	26.9444	776	602176	27.8568
627	393129	25.0400	677	458329	26.0192	727	528529	26.9629	777	603729	27.8747
628	394384	25.0599	678	459684	26.0384	728	529984	26.9815	778	605284	27.8927
629	395641	25.0799	679	461041	26.0576	729	531441	27.0000	779	606841	27.9106
630	396900	25.0998	680	462400	26.0768	730	532900	27.0185	780	608400	27.9285
631	398161	25.1197	681	463761	26.0960	731	534361	27.0370	781	609961	27.9464
632	399424	25.1396	682	465124	26.1151	732	535824	27.0555	782	611524	27.9643
633	400689	25.1595	683	466489	26.1343	733	537289	27.0740	783	613089	27.9821
634	401956	25.1794	684	467856	26.1534	734	538756	27.0924	784	614656	28.0000
635	403225	25.1992	685	469225	26.1725	735	540225	27.1109	785	616225	28.0179
636	404496	25.2190	686	470596	26.1916	736	541696	27.1293	786	617796	28.0357
637	405769	25.2389	687	471969	26.2107	737	543169	27.1477	787	619369	28.0535
638	407044	25.2587	688	273344	26.2298	738	544644	27.1662	788	620944	28.0713
639	408321	25.2784	689	474721	26.2488	739	546121	27.1846	789	622521	28.0891
640	409600	25.2982	690	476100	26.2679	740	547600	27.2029	790	624100	28.1069
641	410881	25.3180	691	477481	26.2869	741	549081	27.2213	791	625681	28.1247
642	412164	25.3377	692	478864	26.3059	742	550564	27.2397	792	627264	28.1425
643	413449	25.3574	693	480249	26.3249	743	552049	27.2580	793	628849	28.1603
644	414736	25.3772	694	481636	26.3439	744	553536	27.2764	794	630436	28.1780
645	416025	25.3969	695	483025	26.3629	745	555025	27.2947	795	632025	28.1957
646	417316	25.4165	696	484416	26.3818	746	556516	27.3130	796	633616	28.2135
647	418609	25.4362	697	485809	26.4008	747	558009	27.3313	797	635209	28.2312
648	419904	25.4558	698	487204	26.4197	748	559504	27.3496	798	636804	28.2489
649	421201	25.4755	699	488601	26.4386	749	561001	27.3679	799	638401	28.2666
650	422500	25.4951	700	490000	26.4575	750	562500	27.3861	800	640000	28.2843

n	n^2	$\sqrt{n}$	n	n^2	$\sqrt{n}$	n	n^2	$\sqrt{n}$	n	n^2	$\sqrt{n}$
801	641601	28.3019	851	724201	29.1719	901	811801	30.0167	951	904401	30.8383
802	643204	28.3196	852	725904	29.1890	902	813604	30.0333	952	906304	30.8545
803	644809	28.3373	853	727609	29.2062	903	815409	30.0500	953	908209	30.8707
804	646416	28.3549	854	729316	29.2233	904	817216	30.0666	954	910116	30.8869
805	648025	28.3725	855	731025	29.2404	905	819025	30.0832	955	912025	30.9031
806	649636	28.3901	856	732736	29.2575	906	820836	30.0998	956	913936	30.9192
807	651249	28.4077	857	734449	29.2746	907	822649	30.1164	957	915849	30.9354
808	652864	28.4253	858	736164	29.2916	908	824464	30.1330	958	917764	30.9516
809	654481	28.4429	859	737881	29.3087	909	826281	30.1496	959	919681	30.9677
810	656100	28.4605	860	739600	29.3258	910	828100	30.1662	960	921600	30.9839
811	657721	28.4781	861	741321	29.3428	911	829921	30.1828	961	923521	31.0000
812	659344	28.4956	862	743044	29.3598	912	831744	30.1993	962	925444	31.0161
813	660969	28.5132	863	744769	29.3769	913	833569	30.2159	963	927369	31.0322
814	662596	28.5307	864	746496	29.3939	914	835396	30.2324	964	929296	31.0483
815	664225	28.5482	865	748225	29.4109	915	837225	30.2490	965	931225	31.0644
816	665856	28.5657	866	749956	29.4279	916	839056	30.2655	966	933156	31.0805
817	667489	28.5832	867	751689	29.4449	917	840889	30.2820	967	935089	31.0966
818	669124	28.6007	868	753424	29.4618	918	842724	30.2985	968	937024	31.1127
819	670761	28.6182	869	755161	29.4788	919	844561	30.3150	969	938961	31.1288
820	672400	28.6356	870	756900	29.4958	920	846400	30.3315	970	940900	31.1448
821	674041	28.6531	871	758641	29.5127	921	848241	30.3480	971	942841	31.1609
822	675684	28.6705	872	760384	29.5296	922	850084	30.3645	972	944784	31.1769
823	677329	28.6880	873	762129	29.5466	923	851929	30.3809	973	946729	31.1929
824	678976	28.7054	874	763876	29.5635	924	853776	30.3974	974	948676	31.2090
825	680625	28.7228	875	765625	29.5804	925	855625	30.4138	975	950625	31.2250
826	682276	28.7402	876	767376	29.5973	926	857476	30.4302	976	952576	31.2410
827	683929	28.7576	877	769129	29.6142	927	859329	30.4467	977	954529	31.2570
828	685584	28.7750	878	770884	29.6311	928	861184	30.4631	978	956484	31.2730
829	687241	28.7924	879	772641	29.6479	929	863041	30.4795	979	958441	31.2890
830	688900	28.8097	880	774400	29.6648	930	864900	30.4959	980	960400	31.3050
831	690561	28.8271	881	776161	29.6816	931	866761	30.5123	981	962361	31.3209
832	692224	28.8444	882	777924	29.6985	932	868624	30.5287	982	964324	31.3369
833	693889	28.8617	883	779689	29.7153	933	870489	30.5450	983	966289	31.3528
834	695556	28.8791	884	781456	29.7321	934	872356	30.5614	984	968256	31.3688
835	697225	28.8964	885	783225	29.7489	935	874225	30.5778	985	970225	31.3847
836	698896	28.9137	886	784996	29.7658	936	876096	30.5941	986	972196	31.4006
837	700569	28.9310	887	786769	29.7825	937	877969	30.6105	987	974169	31.4166
838	702244	28.9482	888	788544	29.7993	938	879844	30.6268	988	976144	31.4325
839	703921	28.9655	889	790321	29.8161	939	881721	30.6431	989	978121	31.4484
840	705600	28.9828	890	792100	29.8329	940	883600	30.6594	990	980100	31.4643
841	707281	29.0000	891	793881	29.8496	941	885481	30.6757	991	982081	31.4802
842	708964	29.0172	892	795664	29.8664	942	887364	30.6920	992	984064	31.4960
843	710649	29.0345	893	797449	29.8831	943	889249	30.7083	993	986049	31.5119
844	712336	29.0517	894	799236	29.8998	944	891136	30.7246	994	988036	31.5278
845	714025	29.0689	895	801025	29.9166	945	893025	30.7409	995	990025	31.5436
846	715716	29.0861	896	802816	29.9333	946	894916	30.7571	996	992016	31.5595
847	717409	29.1033	897	804609	29.9500	947	896809	30.7734	997	994009	31.5753
848	719104	29.1204	898	806404	29.9666	948	898704	30.7896	998	996004	31.5911
849	720801	29.1376	899	808201	29.9833	949	900601	30.8058	999	998001	31.6070
850	722500	29.1548	900	810000	30.0000	950	902500	30.8221			

INDEX